STE

C000126831

AQA GCSE Combined Science
Lab Book

Contents

Published by Pearson Education Limited, 80 Strand, London, WC2R 0RL.
www.pearsonschoolsandfecolleges.co.uk

Text © Mark Levesley, Penny Johnson, Sue Kearsey, Iain Brand, Carol Tear, Nigel Saunders, Sue Robilliard, and Pearson Education Limited 2018
Series editor: Stella Paes
Designed by Pete Stratton, Pearson Education Ltd.
Edited by Haremi Ltd.
Typeset by Servis Filmsetting Ltd.
Original illustrations © Pearson Education Limited 2018
Cover design by Pete Stratton
Cover photo/illustration © Shutterstock: Alex Staroseltsev

First published 2017
Second edition 2018

19 18
10 9 8 7 6 5 4 3 2 1

British Library Cataloguing in Publication Data
A catalogue record for this book is available from the British Library

ISBN 9781292267821

Acknowledgements
The publishers would like to thank Linda Turner, Helen Sayers and Janet Custard for their contributions to this resource and would like to thank John Kavanagh for his contributions to the previous edition.
The rights of Mark Levesley, Penny Johnson, Sue Kearsey, Iain Brand, Carol Tear, Nigel Saunders and Sue Robilliard to be identified as authors of this work have been asserted by them in accordance with the Copyright, Designs and Patents Act 1988.

Notes from the publisher
We have attempted to identify all the recognised hazards in the practical activities in this guide. The Lab Book and online Technician's notes provide suitable warnings about the hazards and suggests appropriate precautions. Teachers and technicians should remember, however, that where there is a hazard, the employer is required to carry out a risk assessment under either the COSHH Regulations or the Management of Health and Safety at Work Regulations. We have assumed that practical work is carried out in a properly equipped and maintained laboratory and that any fieldwork takes account of the employer's guidelines. In particular, we have assumed that any mains-operated electrical equipment is properly maintained, that students have been shown how to conduct normal laboratory operations (such as heating or handling heavy objects) safely and that good practice is observed when chemicals or living organisms are handled. We have also assumed that classes are sufficiently small and well-behaved for a teacher to be able to exercise adequate supervision of the students and that rooms are not so crowded that students' activities pose a danger to their neighbours.
Science safety experts have reviewed but not trialled this text. Following receipt of the reviews any guidance has been incorporated and the resources updated.

Important note

Neither Pearson, the authors nor the series editor take responsibility for the safety of any activity.
Before doing any practical activity you are legally required to carry out your own risk assessment. In particular, any local rules issued by your employer must be obeyed, regardless of what is recommended in this resource. Where students are required to write their own risk assessments they must always be checked by the teacher and revised, as necessary, to cover any issues the students may have overlooked. The teacher should always have the final control as to how the practical is conducted.
Further sources of information: CLEAPSS, www.cleapss.org.uk (includes Secondary Science Laboratory Handbook and Hazcards).

Specification note
This resource is based on the April 2016 accredited version of the specification. The worksheets in this resource have not been reviewed or endorsed by AQA and should not be considered as being published by AQA. Copies of official specifications for all AQA qualifications may be found on the website: www.aqa.org.uk.
While the Publishers have made every attempt to ensure that advice on the qualification and its assessment is accurate, the official specification and associated assessment guidance materials are the only authoritative source of information and should always be referred to for definitive guidance.

Content accuracy
Pearson has robust editorial processes, including answer and fact checks, to ensure the accuracy of the content in this publication, and every effort is made to ensure this publication is free of errors. We are, however, only human, and occasionally errors do occur. Pearson is not liable for any misunderstandings that arise as a result of errors in this publication, but it is our priority to ensure that the content is accurate. If you spot an error, please do contact us at resourcescorrections@pearson.com so we can make sure it is corrected.

This Combined Science practical workbook is designed to enrich and deepen your understanding of AQA GCSE Science through each of the required practical activities.

We want you to enjoy your science lessons and at the same time feel that you are well-prepared for your final examinations.

Each practical is not a recipe to be merely followed but a step-by-step guide with thought-provoking questions. Each practical can be adapted to suit your school.

The Lab Book provides a clear individual record of practical work linked to the AQA required practical activities.

(Your teacher can also download a practical tracking document from **www.pearsonschools.co.uk/AQApracticalsupport** for your whole class too, as well as answers to exam-style questions.)

Working though this book should:

- Further develop your practical confidence and competence in using a wide range of apparatus and techniques.
- Support you to work carefully and methodically.
- Improve your experimental skills and strategies for planning and adapting laboratory procedures.
- Show you the link between doing practical work and applying your knowledge and understanding of scientific ideas.
- Encourage your use of the language of experimentation, so that you can use words like validity, precision and reproducibility with accuracy and confidence.
- Provide practice in answering new practically-based GCSE questions designed to test the full range of your abilities.
- Support you to 'Work Scientifically'.

  (We recommend that you find out more about what AQA means by checking your specification.)

Working Scientifically and the use of apparatus and techniques is assessed across all of your GCSE Science papers. Examiners will expect you to have completed all of these practical activities yourself and will test what you have learned in a number of ways.

Some examples of the style of the questions you might be asked have been added to each practical activity. They may ask you to:

- Show what you know about these experiments.   (Assessment Objective 1)
- Apply what you know about Working Scientifically
  and test how well you present and analyse data.   (Assessment Objective 2)
- Make sense of results, question evidence, suggest
  improvements and develop conclusions.   (Assessment Objective 3)

This book will help you practise and improve your mathematical skills in science too, especially your use of graphs, equations and how you analyse your results.

We hope that these experiments will trigger your curiosity about science, the scientific process and how scientists perform investigations. We encourage you to ask deeper questions and carry out further investigations, with your teacher's consent.

Stella Paes
Series Editor

aving an investigative mind and carrying out experiments are fundamental to science. The AQA
cience curricuum has carefully selected practical work to:

- enhance the delivered content
- increase enthusiasm for the subject
- promote a more scientifically literate society
- enable students to gain vital transferable skills.

ompleting these required practicals, along with other investigations selected by your teacher,
nables you to have a rich hands-on experience of science as it is meant to be – a dynamic, practical
ubject relevant to everyone.

his Lab Book has been designed to support your practical work, giving you all the instructions
ou need to perform the required practicals, including apparatus and techniques (AT) skills self-
ssessment so that you can track your progress.

very effort has been made to ensure you have the opportunity to cover all of the specification skills
VS – Working scientifically, AT – Use of apparatus and techniques). However, because we provide
ou with the methods, you will not be carrying out a full investigation (WS 2.2).

is hoped that these required practicals will be supplemented by other investigations and
xperiments that you will complete through your GCSE course. However you could carry out your
wn plan, or adapt your plan using the methods presented in this book. Again, plans need to be
sked assessed.

ach practical activity has:

- **Practical Objectives**, which are what you should do that relate directly to the AQA required
practical activities.
- **Content Objectives**, which are what you should know and understand from the AQA
specification that relate directly to this practical.
- **Learning Outcomes**, which are a way for you to track your mastery of key apparatus and
techniques.

Combined science

One of the first people to examine cells using a microscope was Robert Hooke. He examined bark from a cork oak tree and saw little box shapes. He called them 'cells' because he thought the boxes looked like the small rooms (or cells) found in monasteries at the time. Hooke realised that it was important to make accurate drawings of what he saw to help explain his work to others. You are going to examine specimens using a microscope and then make labelled drawings of them.

Your teacher may watch to see if you can:

- handle microscopes and slides carefully and safely.

Core learning outcomes: I am able to…
use appropriate apparatus to record length and area
use a microscope to make observations of biological specimens and produce labelled scientific drawings.

Method 1: Examining pre-prepared slides of cells

A Set up your microscope on the lowest magnification objective lens. Work out the total magnification and measure the diameter of the field of view (by using the microscope to observe a transparent ruler). Record this in the box below.

B Put the next most powerful objective lens in place. Work out the magnification and by how much it has increased from the magnification in step **A** (e.g. moving from a ×10 to a ×50 lens is an increase of 5 times). Now divide the diameter of the field of view from step **A** by the increase in magnification to give you the new diameter of the field of view (e.g. if the field of view in step **A** was 2 mm, then 2 ÷ 5 = 0.4 mm). Do this for each objective lens. Record the total magnification and field of view diameter for each objective lens in the box below.

Practical Objective

To use a microscope to observe cells and sub-cellular structures.

Content Objective

The light microscope allows observation of plant and animal cells and can be used to estimate relative size of cells and some sub-cellular structures.

Apparatus

- light microscope
- lamp
- prepared slides
- transparent ruler

Safety

- Handle slides with care.

Now go back to the lowest magnification objective lens and observe a prepared slide.

Use higher magnifications to observe the cells. Estimate the sizes using your field of view diameters.

Using a sharp pencil, draw four or five cells in the box below. Identify and label the cells' parts using straight ruled lines. Add the magnification and any sizes that you have estimated.

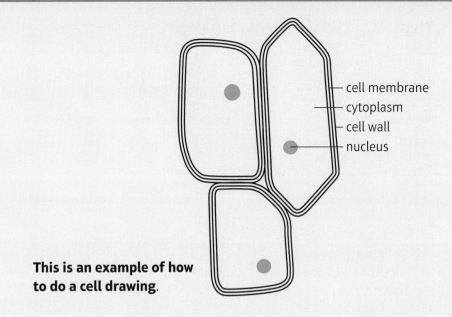

— cell membrane
— cytoplasm
— cell wall
— nucleus

This is an example of how to do a cell drawing.

Method 2: Examining your cheek cells

A Using the pipette, add a small drop of water to the slide.

B Stroke the inside of your cheek gently with the wooden spatula. You only want to collect loose cells, so do not scratch the inside of your mouth.

C Use the end of the spatula that has been in your mouth to stir the drop of water on the slide. Place the used spatula in disinfectant.

D Use a pipette to add a small drop of methylene blue stain. This makes cells easier to see.

E Place a coverslip onto the slide at a 45° angle on one edge of the drop. Then use a toothpick to gently lower the coverslip onto the drop, as shown in the diagram. Avoid trapping air bubbles, which will appear as black-edged circles under a microscope.

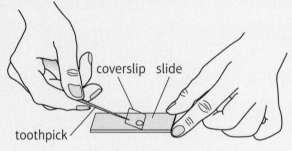

coverslip   slide

toothpick

F Touch a piece of paper towel to any liquid that spreads out from under the coverslip.

G Use the lowest magnification objective lens to observe the slide. The **nuclei** of the cheek cells will be dark blue.

H Use higher magnifications to observe the cells. Estimate the sizes using your field of view diameters.

I Using a sharp pencil, draw two or three cells in the box below. Identify and label the cells' parts using straight ruled lines. Add the magnification and any sizes that you have estimated.

Apparatus

- light microscope
- lamp
- microscope slide
- coverslip
- methylene blue stain
- pipette
- paper towel
- water
- wooden toothpick/ cocktail stick
- sterile wooden spatula/ tongue depressor
- disinfectant

Safety

- Handle slides with care.
- Anything that you have put into your mouth should be placed in disinfectant after use.
- Wear gloves if using stains.
- Wear eye protection.

Method 3: Examining onion cells

Use a pipette to add a drop of iodine solution to a microscope slide.

Using forceps, remove a very small piece of the thin 'skin' on the inside of the fleshy part of the onion. It is quite tricky to handle as it is very thin.

Place the small piece of skin on the drop of iodine on the slide.

Place a coverslip onto the slide at a 45° angle on one edge of the drop. Then use a toothpick to gently lower the coverslip onto the drop, as shown in the diagram.

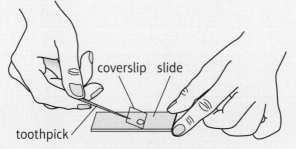

coverslip   slide

toothpick

Avoid trapping air bubbles, which will appear as black-edged circles under a microscope.

Touch a piece of paper towel to any liquid that spreads out from under the coverslip.

Use the lowest magnification objective lens to observe the slide. Then use higher magnifications to observe the cells in more detail. Estimate sizes as you observe.

Using a sharp pencil, draw four or five cells in the box below. Identify and label the cells using straight ruled lines. Add the magnification and any sizes that you have estimated.

Apparatus

- light microscope
- lamp
- microscope slide
- coverslip
- iodine stain
- pipette
- paper towel
- forceps
- wooden toothpick/cocktail stick
- piece of onion bulb
- gloves

Safety ⚠

- Handle slides and microscopes with care.
- Wear gloves if using stains.
- Wear eye protection.

Exam-style questions

01   The diagram shows a plant cell viewed under a light microscope.

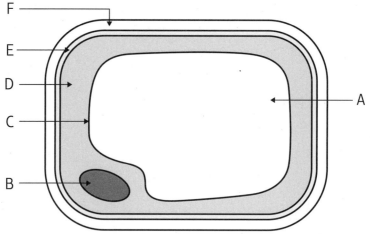

01.1   Which letters label the following structures?   **[2 mar**

Cell wall [ ]   Cytoplasm [ ]

01.2   The cell is taken from the root of the plant.

If the cell were taken from a leaf, which other sub-cellular structure would you expect to
see under a light microscope?   **[1 ma**

_____02M_____ E_____

01.3   The plant cell is 0.1 mm wide. A student estimates that the length of the nucleus is a sixth of the
length of the cell.

Calculate the length of the nucleus. Give your answer in micrometres (μm) and to 3 significant
figures.   **[3 mar**

Answer _____ μm

01.4   Bacterial cells are much smaller than plant cells.

A bacterial cell measures 2.6×10^3 nm. What does the cell measure in μm?   **[1 ma**

Answer _____ μm

he cells in a potato contain many substances dissolved in water. The cells
re surrounded by cell membranes that are permeable to water. When a strip
f potato is placed in a solution, the overall movement of water molecules
etween the potato cells and the solution will depend on which has the
igher concentration of solutes. In this practical, you will investigate osmosis
1 potato strips in terms of the percentage change in mass of potato in
ifferent solutions.

our teacher may watch to see if you can:

measure accurately
work carefully.

Core learning outcomes: I am able to…
use appropriate apparatus to record mass and time
use appropriate apparatus and techniques to observe and measure the process of osmosis
measure the rate of osmosis by water uptake.

Method

Using the waterproof pen, label each tube with the name of one of the
solutions. Place the boiling tubes in the rack, as shown in the diagram.

Dry a potato strip carefully by blotting it with a paper towel. Measure its
mass on the balance.

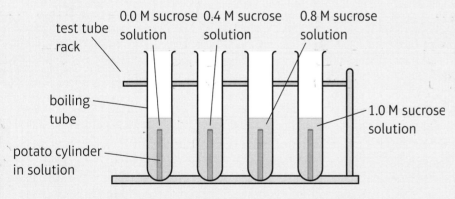

Place the potato strip into one of the tubes. Record the concentration
of sucrose solution and the mass of the strip in your results table
(see next page).

Repeat steps **B** and **C** until all strips have been measured and placed in
tubes.

Carefully fill each tube with the appropriate solution, so the potato
is fully covered. Leave the tubes for at least 30 minutes.

Use the forceps to remove each potato strip from its tube, blot dry on a
paper towel and measure its mass again. Record all the masses in the
results table.

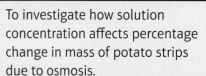

Practical Objective

To investigate how solution
concentration affects percentage
change in mass of potato strips
due to osmosis.

Content Objective

Osmosis is the diffusion of
water from a dilute solution to a
concentrated solution through a
partially permeable membrane.

Apparatus

- four potato strips
- accurate balance
- four boiling tubes and rack (or beakers)
- waterproof pen
- four sucrose solutions: 0.0 M, 0.4 M, 0.8 M and 1.0 M
- forceps
- paper towels

Safety

- Do not drink any of the solutions or eat the potatoes.

Prediction

1 For each of the solutions you will use, predict whether the potato strips will gain mass, lose mass or keep the same mass. Explain your predictions.

Recording your results

2 Complete the first three columns of the table below – Concentration of sucrose solution, **A** and **B** – with the solution descriptions and your measurements from the experiment.

Concentration of sucrose solution (M)	A Mass of potato strip at start (g)	B Mass of potato strip at end (g)	C Change in mass (g) $= B - A$	D % change in mass $= \frac{C}{A} \times 100\%$
0 M	6.4g	6.4g	0	$\frac{0}{6.4} \times 100 = 0.$
0.2M	6.4g	6.5g	+0.1g	1.56
0.4M	6.4g	6.5g	+0.1g	1.56
0.6 M	6.4g	6.6g	+0.2g	3.10

3 Complete column **C** by calculating the change in mass for each potato strip using the formula shown. Make sure the sign is included when writing down values for columns **C** and **D** because this reveals whether mass is gained or lost.

4 Complete column **D** by calculating the percentage change in mass for each potato strip using the formula show

5 Compare the results for percentage change in mass from all the groups in the class. For each solution, identify any results that seem very different from the others (anomalous results).
Try to suggest a reason why they are so different.

| 0.8M | 6.4g | 6.3g | ⁻0.1g | -1.56 |
| 1.0M | 6.4g | 6.2g | ⁻0.2g | -3.10 |

Excluding any anomalous results, calculate a mean value for percentage change in mass for each solution.

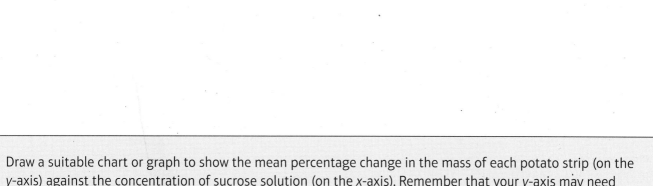

Draw a suitable chart or graph to show the mean percentage change in the mass of each potato strip (on the y-axis) against the concentration of sucrose solution (on the x-axis). Remember that your y-axis may need positive and negative numbers.

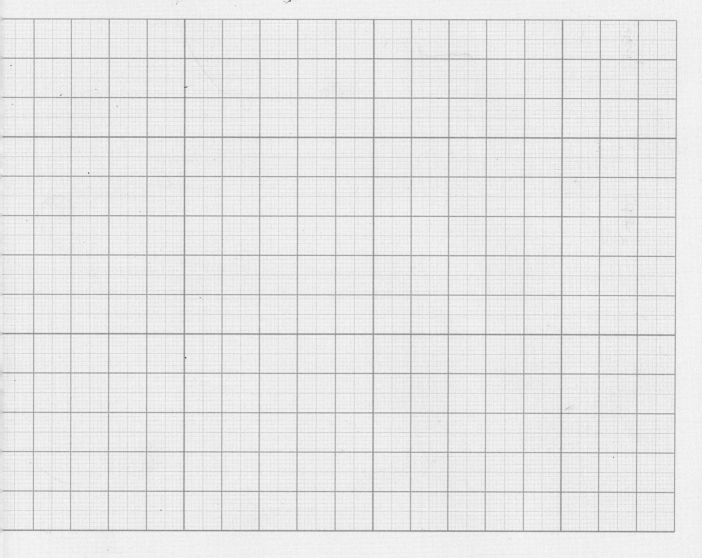

Considering your results/conclusions

8 Describe and explain the pattern shown in your chart or graph. Use the word 'osmosis' in your answer.

9 Explain why you calculated percentage change in mass.

10 Explain why calculating a mean value from several repeats of the same experiment is more likely to give a value that can be reproduced by others.

Evaluation

11 Describe any problems you had with the experiment. Suggest how these could be reduced or avoided to produce better results.

12 Explain how you could use your results to calculate the rate of osmosis in potato cells in 0.4 M sucrose solution.

Exam-style questions

1 Red blood cells were placed in different concentrations of sodium chloride. After two hours, the samples were examined to find the percentage of the cells that had burst. The results are shown in the table below.

Sodium chloride concentration (g/100 cm³)	0.32	0.36	0.40	0.44	0.48
Percentage of red blood cells that burst	100	90	44	15	0

1.1 The different concentrations were made by diluting a stock solution of sodium chloride of concentration 1.0 g/100 cm³ with distilled water.
Describe how to make 10 cm³ of 0.40 g/100 cm³ sodium chloride solution. **[2 marks]**

1.2 Explain why all the red blood cells burst when placed in the 0.32 g/100 cm³ sodium chloride solution. **[3 marks]**

1.3 Onion cells were placed in the same range of sodium chloride solutions. Explain why none of the onion cells burst. **[1 mark]**

1.4 If a kidney is diseased and not working, the person may be sent for dialysis. Waste materials from the blood diffuse across a partially permeable membrane into the dialysis fluid. The dialysis fluid has glucose and salts in it.
Suggest **two** problems that might occur if the dialysis fluid were pure water. **[2 marks]**

By law, all packaged food and drink must be labelled to show how much fat, sugar, protein and some other substances it contains. This is to help customers make informed choices about what they eat and drink. Every new food or drink that is developed must be tested to produce the information needed for the labelling. You will be given a range of powdered foods. Use the food tests below to identify whether each food contains the substances that the reagents test for. Use your results to help you identify the foods from the list you are given. Remember to wipe the spatula and stirrer clean between tests (using a paper towel) to prevent cross-contamination.

Your teacher may watch to see if you can:

- follow instructions carefully
- work safely, reducing the risk of harm from hazards.

Core learning outcomes: I am able to…
safely use a water bath and electric heater
use qualitative reagents to identify biological molecules.

Method

Iodine test for starch

A   Place one spatula of powdered food on a dish.

B   Using a dropper, place a few drops of iodine solution onto the food.

C   Record the name of the food and any change in the colour of the solution.

Benedict's test for reducing sugars

D   Place one spatula of powdered food into a test tube. Add about $1\,cm^3$ of water to the tube and stir to mix.

E   Add an equal volume of Benedict's solution and mix.

F   Place the tube in a water bath at about 95 °C for a few minutes.

G   Record the letter of the food and the colour of the solution.

Biuret test for protein

H   Place one spatula of powdered food into a test tube. Add about $1\,cm^3$ of water to the tube and stir to mix.

I   Add an equal volume of potassium hydroxide (Biuret B) solution to the tube and stir.

J   Add two drops of copper sulfate (Biuret A) solution and stir.

K   Record the name of the food and the colour of the solution after a few minutes.

Emulsion test for lipids

L   Place one spatula of powdered food into a test tube.

M   Add $2\,cm^3$ of ethanol to the tube. Place a bung firmly in the end of the tube and shake the tube vigorously.

N   Allow the contents to settle.

O   Pour the liquid from the top of the mixture into a test tube half filled with water.

P   Record the name of the food and whether the water is cloudy or clear.

Practical Objective

To identify starch, reducing sugars proteins and lipids in foods.

Content Objective

The digestive system is a system in which several organs work together to break down large molecules into smaller, more soluble molecules so that they can be absorbed as food.

Apparatus

- eye protection
- water
- measuring cylinder
- spatula
- powdered foods
- paper towels
- test tubes, racks and bungs
- stirrer
- iodine solution in dropper bottle
- Benedict's solution
- potassium hydroxide (Biuret B) solution
- copper sulfate (Biuret A) solution
- ethanol
- cold water
- electric waterbath at 95 °C

Safety

- Wear eye protection.
- Wash any splashes from skin quickly.
- Do not taste any of the food substances.
- Ethanol (IDA) is hazardous, harmful and highly flammable Keep it away from flames.
- Copper sulfate is poisonous and potassium hydroxide is corrosive (both substances are also present in Benedict's solution). Handle solutions with care and wipe up any spills.
- Avoid scalding with hot water

Combined science

Recording your results

Record your results in the table. There is space below the table to add more rows if needed.

Food	Colour at end of ...			
	iodine test	Benedict's test	Biuret test	emulsion test

Considering your results/conclusions

Which foods contained:

a starch

b reducing sugar

c protein

d lipid?

Do any of your tests give an indication of how much of a substance a food contains? Give a reason for your answer.

Evaluation

Identify any problems you had with this experiment. Explain how the method could be improved to reduce or avoid these errors.

Exam-style questions

01 A student has three bottles. All the labels have fallen off, but the three solutions are:

- starch
- amylase
- albumen (egg white).

The student does some tests on the solution in each bottle.

Test reagent	Final colour		
	Solution 1	Solution 2	Solution 3
Iodine	Blue/black	Yellow	Yellow
Biuret	Pale blue	Lilac	Lilac

01.1 The student decides that **solution 1** is the starch solution. Explain how this decision was made. **[1 mar**

01.2 The student mixes equal volumes of the starch solution with **solution 2** and **solution 3**, and incubates both mixtures at 37 °C for 20 minutes.

Test reagent	Final colour	
	Starch solution and solution 2 mixture	Starch solution and solution 3 mixture
Benedict's	Blue	Brick red

Identify what **solution 2** and **solution 3** are. Explain your decisions using evidence from both the results tables. **[6 mar**

Solution 2:

Explanation:

Solution 3:

Explanation:

Amylase is an enzyme made in the salivary glands in your mouth and in the pancreas. It catalyses the breakdown of starch into smaller sugar molecules. The iodine test identifies the presence of starch, but does not react with sugar. You will use this test to show how effective amylase is in digesting starch at different pHs.

Your teacher may watch to see if you can:

- work safely
- collect accurate data.

Core learning outcomes: I am able to…
use appropriate apparatus to record time, pH and the volumes of liquids
safely use a water bath
measure the rate of reaction by the colour change of iodine indicator
use qualitative iodine reagent to identify starch by continuous sampling.

Method

Pipette one drop of iodine solution into each depression of the dimple tile.

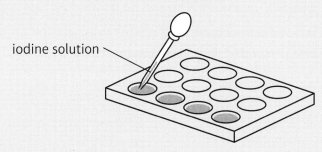

iodine solution

Use a syringe to place 2 cm³ of amylase solution into a test tube.

Add 1 cm³ of your pH solution to the test tube using a second syringe. Record the pH of the solution that you are using.

Using a third syringe, add 2 cm³ of starch solution to a second test tube.

Stand the test tubes from steps **B** and **D** in the water bath. When the liquid in the tubes reaches 30 °C, pour the starch solution into the amylase solution and start the stop clock. Use the pipette to stir the mixture.

After 20 seconds, take a small amount of the mixture in the pipette and place one drop of it on the first iodine drop on the tile. Return the rest of the solution in the pipette to the test tube.

If the iodine solution turns black, there is still starch in the mixture and you should repeat step **F** after 10 seconds. If the iodine solution remains yellow, all the starch has been digested and you should record the time taken for this to happen.

If there is time, repeat the experiment using a solution with a different pH.

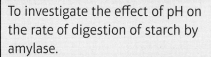

Practical Objective

To investigate the effect of pH on the rate of digestion of starch by amylase.

Content Objective

Amylase is a carbohydrase enzyme that breaks down starch into soluble sugars.

Apparatus

- eye protection
- iodine solution in dropping bottle
- dimple tile
- test tubes
- test-tube rack
- syringes
- pipette
- amylase solution
- starch solution
- solutions of specific pH
- stop clock
- beaker of warm water at 30 °C to act as a water bath
- thermometer

Safety

- Wear eye protection.

Prediction

1   Predict at which pH the amylase will digest starch fastest. Explain your prediction.

Recording your results

2   Collect data from all of the groups in the class so you have results for each of the different pHs. Draw a table in the box below to present these results.

3   If you have more than one result for any pH, use the space below to calculate the mean time. Add the mean times to your results table.

Considering your results

In the space below, plot a line graph to show the time taken for amylase to digest starch at different pHs.

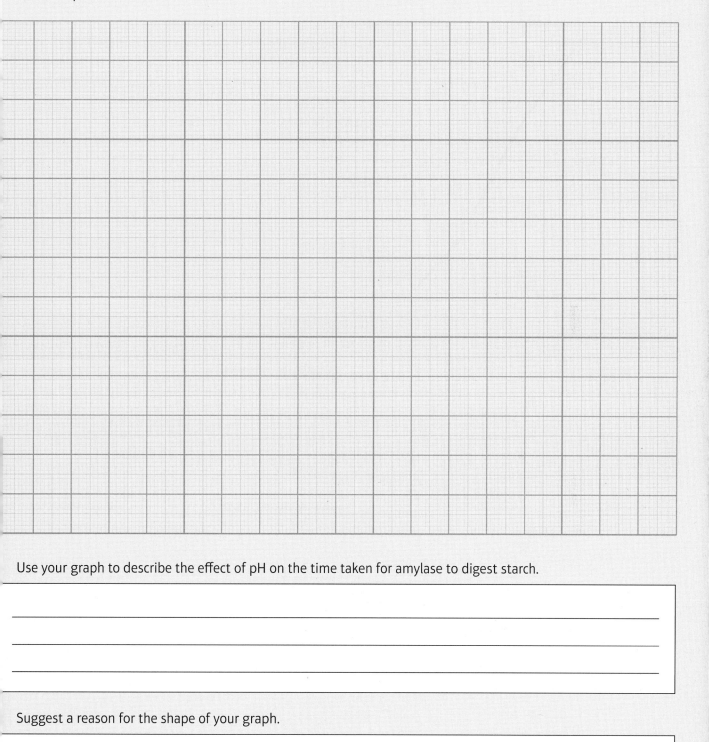

Use your graph to describe the effect of pH on the time taken for amylase to digest starch.

Suggest a reason for the shape of your graph.

7 Some tests are qualitative (they will only show whether the substance is present or not). Other tests are semi-quantitative (they will provide approximate values of how much might be present, e.g. 'little', 'some' or 'a lot'). In this practical, iodine solution was used to detect whether starch was present or not. Is this test qualitative or semi-quantitative?

Explain your answer.

8 Describe any problems you had when carrying out the experiment.

9 Suggest reasons for these problems and ideas for how the method could be changed to help reduce them.

10 Are any of the results surprising? If so, why?

11 Do you think you have enough results to support your conclusion? Explain your answer.

Exam-style questions

1   Pepsin is a protease enzyme produced by the stomach. When pepsin breaks down the protein in egg white, the egg white changes from cloudy to clear.

A student did an investigation into pepsin activity.

This is the method they used.

1.   Put $1\,cm^3$ water, $1\,cm^3$ pepsin and $5\,cm^3$ egg white in a test tube labelled **A**.
2.   Put $2\,cm^3$ water and $5\,cm^3$ egg white in a test tube labelled **B**.
3.   Leave test tubes **A** and **B** for 15 minutes and record the results.

1.1   Explain why the contents of tube **A** became clear after 15 minutes.   **[1 mark]**

1.2   Explain why the contents of tube **B** stayed cloudy after 15 minutes.   **[1 mark]**

1.3   Why did the student add water to tube **A**?   **[1 mark]**

1.4   The student decides to investigate the effect of the concentration of pepsin on the rate of digestion of egg white. Explain how the student can vary the concentration of pepsin.   **[1 mark]**

1.5   The student knows that temperature and pH also affect the rate of reaction of enzymes and that these variables should be controlled.

Suggest suitable values to use for pH and temperature. Give reasons for your choices and say how the student should control these variables.   **[4 marks]**

pH value:

Reason for choice:

Method of control:

Temperature value:

Reason for choice:

Method of control:

icroscopic algae have cells that contain chloroplasts, like plant leaf cells.
he algae can be trapped in jelly balls to make them easier to handle. You
ill put algal balls in an indicator that changes colour as carbon dioxide
vels change. Under normal conditions the indicator is a red colour, but this
anges to yellow at higher carbon dioxide concentrations and purple at
wer carbon dioxide concentrations.[1]

our teacher may watch to see if you can:

- follow instructions carefully
- work safely.

ore learning outcomes: I am able to…
se appropriate apparatus to record the rate of change in carbon dioxide evels and to measure and control the temperature of the water in the heat shield' beaker
afely use a thermometer to measure and control the temperature of the vater in the 'heat shield' beaker
se appropriate apparatus and techniques to observe and measure the rocess of change of carbon dioxide levels
afely and ethically use and dispose of living algae
neasure the rate of reaction by colour change of indicator according to pH.

ethod

Decide the different distances you are going to use between the algae
and the lamp. You will need one clear glass bottle for each distance.
You will also need one extra bottle.

Add 10–15 algal balls to each
bottle. (The same number of algal
balls should be added to each
bottle.)

Add the same volume of indicator
solution to each bottle and put on
the bottle caps.

Your teacher will have a chart or
a range of bottles showing the
colours of the indicator at different
pHs. Compare the colour in your
bottles with this pH range to work
out the pH at the start.

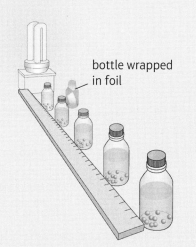

bottle wrapped
in foil

Set up a heat filter between the lamp and where you will place your bottles. The heat filter is a water-filled bottle
or other clear container. Take great care not to spill water near the lamp. Set up a cardboard barrier on the three
sides of the lamp that do not face the glass bottles.

Cover one bottle in kitchen foil, so that it is in the dark.

Place your bottles at measured distances from the lamp. Put the bottle covered in kitchen foil next to the bottle
that is closest to the lamp.

Turn on the lamp and time 60 minutes (or longer).

Practical Objective

To find out how light
intensity affects the **rate** of
photosynthesis.

Content Objective

Photosynthesis is an endothermic
reaction in which energy is
transferred to chloroplasts by
light. The rate of photosynthesis
is affected by light intensity,
carbon dioxide concentration and
temperature.

Apparatus

- eye protection
- bijou bottles and caps
- beaker of algal balls
- hydrogencarbonate indicator
- high lumen output lamp (> 1000 lumen bulb) and heat filter
- metre rule
- measuring cylinder
- kitchen foil
- stop clock
- plastic forceps/spoon

Safety

- Wear eye protection.
- Wash your hands after setting up the experiment.
- Avoid touching the hot lamp.
- Using cardboard, shield the three sides of the lamp that do not face the glass bottles.

note to teachers: The full title of this required practical is 'Investigate the effect of light intensity on the rate of photosynthesis using
aquatic organism such as pondweed'. The traditional method uses counting bubbles of oxygen or measuring the gas produced using
ndweed, and schools may also wish to carry out this experiment to fulfil AQA's criteria. However, the practical given here has proved
be a more successful variant of investigating light intensity.

I   Compare the colours of all your bottles with those of the pH range bottles.

J   Record the pHs of the solutions in your bottles in a suitable table.

Recording your results

1   Record your results in the table below.

Distance from lamp to bottle (cm)	pH at start	pH at end	Rate of photosynthesis (change in pH/hou

Considering your results/conclusions

2   **a**   For each bottle, calculate the rate of photosynthesis as the change in pH per hour. Algae also respire. Respiration produces carbon dioxide, which lowers the pH. Therefore only use values where the change in pH is positive.

change in pH = pH at end – pH at start

$$rate = \frac{change\ in\ pH}{time\ (in\ hours)}$$

     b   Use your calculations to complete the last column of the table above.

3   Plot your results on a scatter graph. Plot the variable that you have changed (the independent variable) on the x-axis. Plot the rate of photosynthesis on the y-axis.

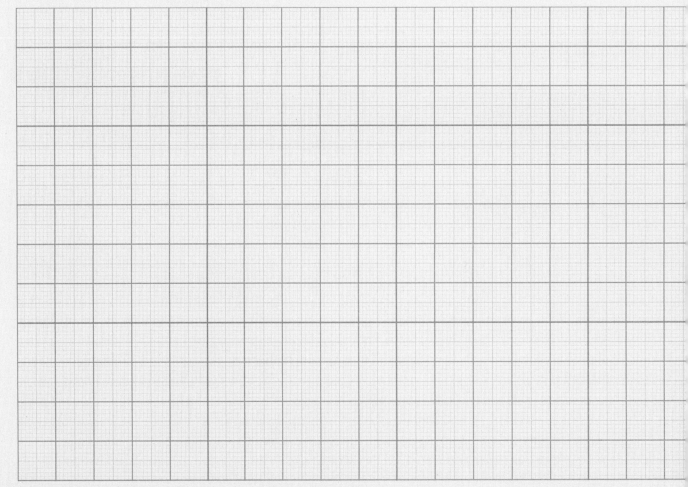

Considering your results/conclusions

4 a Describe the pattern shown on your graph.

b Explain why this pattern is observed.

5 H Light intensity can be calculated using the inverse square law. Calculate the light intensity for each distance using the formula Light intensity = $1/d^2$ where d is the distance from the lamp to the bottle of algae.
Sketch the shape of the graph of light intensity on the x-axis and rate of photosynthesis on the y-axis.

Evaluation

6 Explain the purpose of the tube covered in foil.

Exam-style questions

01.1 Green plants are able to make their own food.

Complete the sentences below, using the words from the box. **[3 marks**

oxygen	transpiration	hydrogen	photosynthesis
nitrogen	respiration	carbon dioxide	

Green plants use light energy to produce their own food by absorbing _____ gas from the

air and water from the soil. _____ gas is released as a by-product. The process is called

_____.

01.2 What measurements would you need to take to calculate the rate of photosynthesis? **[2 mark**

01.3 Sodium hydrogencarbonate can be used to increase the amount of carbon dioxide in the water surrounding
pondweed.

Describe a method you could use to investigate the effect of carbon dioxide concentration on the rate of
photosynthesis. Use the apparatus in the diagram below in your method.

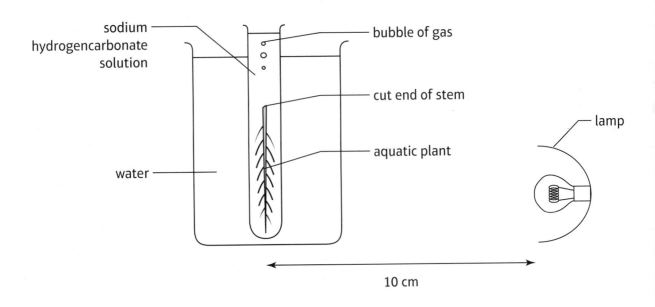

You should include:

- how you will change the independent variable
- how you will control other variables. **[6 marks]**

_____
_____
_____
_____
_____
_____

01.4 The graph shows the effect of light intensity on the rate of photosynthesis at two different concentrations of carbon dioxide (CO_2).

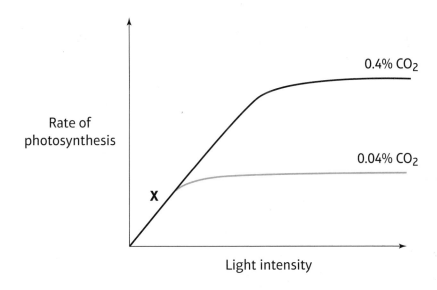

Suggest which factor is limiting the rate of photosynthesis at point **X**. **[1 mark]**

_____
_____

01.5 Explain why the rate of photosynthesis increases when the carbon dioxide concentration is increased. **[1 mark]**

_____
_____

We need to respond to changes in our environment. Sometimes these responses need to be rapid so that we are protected from an imminent threat, for example an object travelling towards us very quickly. The time taken for us to react is known as our reaction time. You are going to undertake a simple investigation into reaction times. You will need to analyse the results to see if faster reaction times can be linked to skills or experiences, e.g. being proficient at reactive computer games.

Your teacher may watch to see if you can:

- follow instructions carefully
- work safely.

Core learning outcomes: I am able to…
select appropriate apparatus and techniques to measure the process of reaction time
safely and ethically use humans to measure physiological function of reaction time and responses to a chosen factor.

Method

A The person who is having their reactions tested should sit down on the chair with their weaker arm (not the one they normally write with) placed on the table. Their hand should be overhanging the table edge.

B The tester holds a ruler vertically between the outstretched index finger and thumb of the person being tested. The finger and thumb should not be touching the ruler. The top of the thumb should be level with the zero mark on the ruler.

C The tester releases the ruler without telling the person being tested. The person being tested has to catch the ruler as quickly as possible.

D When the person catches the ruler, record the number that is level with the top of their hand. Record the length of the drop in the table below. Repeat the drop five times and calculate an average.

E Now swap roles and repeat steps **A** to **D**. If your group is larger than two, repeat the steps for each person.

F Find out who has the fastest reaction time.

Practical Objective

To find out who has the fastest reactions.

Content Objective

The nervous system allows humans to react to their surroundings and coordinate their behaviour.

Apparatus

- metre rule
- bench or table
- chair or stool
- a partner

Safety

- When the ruler is falling, it could fall in different directions. Take care that it does not hit anyone.

Ruler measurements (cm)				
Drop	**Person 1**	**Person 2**	**Person 3**	**Person 4**
First drop				
Second drop				
Third drop				
Fourth drop				
Fifth drop				
Average drop				

considering your results/conclusions

Draw a suitable graph or chart to show your results.

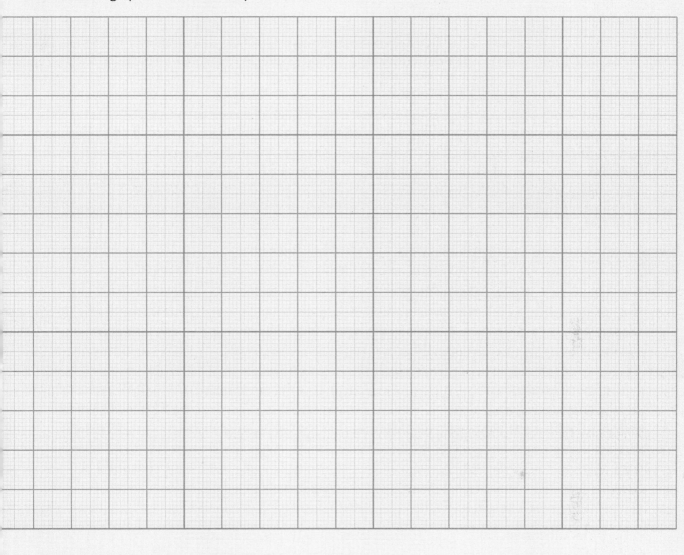

a Who has the fastest reaction time? Explain your answer.

_____

_____

b Is there any reason why this person has the fastest reaction time?
(Hint: Think whether this person plays lots of video games or is good at sports with fast reaction times.)

_____

_____

_____

_____

3 Did the reaction times increase or decrease from the first drop to the fifth drop? Explain any pattern you can see in your results.

Evaluation

4 What could you do to improve this experiment?

5 Suggest a different way to test reaction times.

Exam-style questions

1.1 All nervous control systems are made up of receptors, coordinators and effectors.

Draw in lines to show which of the boxed items on the right is a receptor, coordinator or effector. **[3 marks]**

Receptor	Brain and spinal cord
	Cell in retina of the eye
Coordinator	Pancreas
	Muscle in the arm
Effector	Nerve cell in finger tip

1.2 Your reaction times can be measured by using a computer program. One example of how this works is by having to click when a box changes from red to green.

A student wants to compare reaction times using this computer program.

Suggest which **three** variables need to be controlled. **[3 marks]**

1 _____

2 _____

3 _____

1.3 Give a reason why some males would have difficulty spotting the colour change. **[2 marks]**

_____

_____

A transect is used to study the distribution of organisms and how it is affected by changes in environmental conditions. With a belt transect, quadrats are placed at regular intervals along the transect line to sample the organisms. You will use a belt transect to study the effect of abiotic factors on the abundance of low-growing plants. The transect will stretch between open ground and heavy shade under a large tree. Several abiotic factors will vary along the transect. Before you start, you will need to decide which abiotic factors to measure and how to measure them. You will also need to decide which plants to record and how you will record their abundance within each quadrat.

Your teacher may watch to see if you can:

- work efficiently
- follow safety guidance.

Core learning outcomes: I am able to…
use appropriate apparatus to record length and area
use transect lines and quadrats to measure distribution of a species
safely and ethically use organisms to record their response to a factor in the environment
apply appropriate sampling techniques to investigate the distribution and abundance of organisms in an ecosystem via direct use in the field
use appropriate techniques in more complex contexts including continuous sampling in an investigation.

Method

A You are going to investigate the distribution of a particular plant species. Choose from: dandelions, daisies or buttercups. (Your teacher might suggest an alternative plant that is found in the local area.) If your teacher has not told you where to place the transect, look for somewhere that shows obvious variation in environmental conditions, such as from bright light to deep shade under a tree, or from an area that shows heavy trampling to an area with less trampling.

B Decide which environmental factors you will measure and how you will measure them.

C Peg out the tape measure along the ground to form the transect line.

D Take measurements at regular intervals along the transect line (as shown in the diagram). Decide on your measurement intervals, which may depend on how long the line is and how much time you have to record information.

E Place the top left-hand corner of the quadrat at a measurement point on the transect line.

F Measure the environmental factors at that point and record them.

G Record the abundance of your selected organism (this is the plant species you chose earlier) in the quadrat.

H Repeat steps **F** and **G** at each measurement point along the transect.

Practical Objective

To investigate the distribution of a species using a transect and quadrats.

Content Objective

Ecologists use a range of methods with transects and quadrats to determine the abundance and distribution of species in an ecosystem.

Apparatus

- long tape measure (at least 20 m) with pegs at each end
- quadrat (e.g. 50 cm × 50 cm square)
- apparatus for measuring suitable abiotic factors, e.g. light sensor and recorder, soil humidity sensor, anemometer (wind speed measurer)
- *optional:* identification charts and pencil

Safety

- Follow any safety guidance related to the working area.
- Consider the safety aspects of your chosen site, such as poisonous plants, animal faeces or open water, and take appropriate precautions while working.
- Wash your hands after the experiment.

Recording your results

In the space below, draw a table to record the abundance of the organism you sampled at each point along the transect line as well as the environmental factor measurements at each point.

2 Draw a suitable chart or graph to show your results.

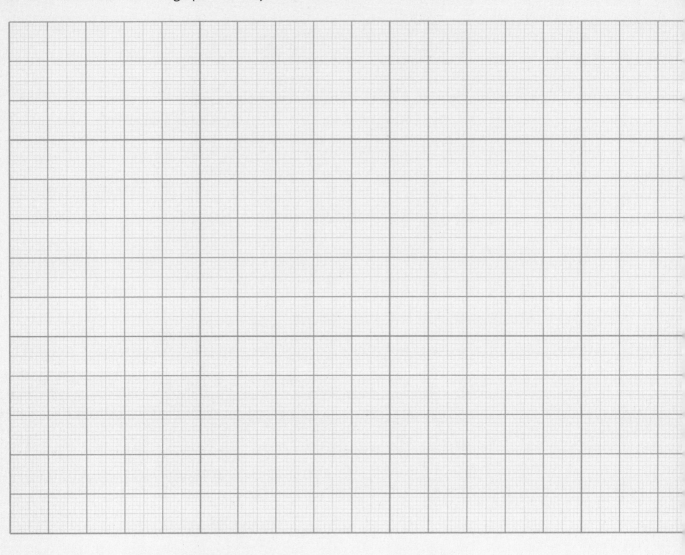

Considering your results/conclusions

3 Describe the change in distribution of your chosen organism along the transect.

4 Describe the change in your chosen environmental factor along the transect.

Describe any correlation between the change in distribution of the organism and the change in environmental factor.

Suggest an explanation for any correlation that you have described in question **5**.

Evaluation

Describe an experiment you could do in the lab to test whether the environmental factor you measured affects the organism as you suggest in your answer to question **6**.

Exam-style questions

01 A lawn weed killer will kill broad-leaved weeds but not grass.

An area of lawn was divided in two, with one half treated with lawn weed killer.

This is the method used.

1. In each area, a student laid out two tapes at right angles to form axes.
2. A calculator was used to generate random numbers for coordinates.
3. A quadrat was placed at each pair of coordinates.
4. The number of dandelion plants in each quadrat was counted.

01.1 Why were the sites of the quadrat chosen at random? **[1 mar**

01.2 Calculate the mean number of dandelions per quadrat in the treated lawn. Write your answer in the table below. **[1 mar**

Quadrat number	Number of dandelion plants	
	Treated lawn	Untreated lawn
1	2	6
2	0	4
3	1	7
4	0	3
5	0	5
6	1	8
7	5	1
8	0	3
9	2	9
10	1	6
Mean number of dandelions per quadrat		5.2
Estimated total number of dandelions in area of lawn		4160

01.3 The area of the quadrat is 0.25 m². Each area of lawn is 200 m².

Calculate the estimated number of dandelions in the treated lawn. Write your answer in the table above. **[2 mark**

01.4 How effective was the lawn weed killer? Explain your answer using results from the investigation. **[3 mark**

Salts, such as copper sulfate, are compounds formed by reacting an acid with a base. Copper oxide reacts with warm sulfuric acid to produce a blue solution of the salt copper sulfate. In this practical, you will use these reactants to prepare pure, dry, hydrated copper sulfate crystals.

Your teacher may watch to see if you can:
- safely and correctly use the apparatus.

Core learning outcomes: I am able to…
safely use appropriate heating devices and techniques including a Bunsen burner, water bath or electric heater
use appropriate apparatus, techniques and reagents for conducting chemical reactions
safely use a range of equipment to purify and/or separate chemical mixtures including by evaporation, filtration, crystallisation
safely use and carefully handle liquids and solids, including carefully mixing reagents under controlled conditions.

Method

1. Wearing safety goggles, pour about 40 cm³ of dilute sulfuric acid into a beaker.

2. Set up the gauze, tripod and heatproof mat. Using the Bunsen burner, heat the acid *gently* until it is almost boiling. Turn off the Bunsen burner.

3. Use the spatula to add a small amount of copper oxide to the acid and stir with the rod.

4. Keep adding small amounts of copper oxide until the black powder does not disappear after stirring. (This makes sure the copper oxide is in excess.)

5. Filter the mixture into a beaker and pour into an evaporating basin.

Step E

6. Make a water bath by half filling a 250 cm³ beaker with water. Place the evaporating basin on top of it. Heat the beaker, evaporating basin and contents using a Bunsen burner on a blue flame.

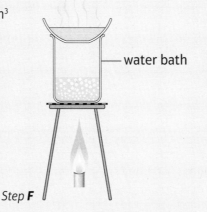

— water bath

7. Heat until about half of the water in the water bath has evaporated. Then allow the evaporating basin to cool.

8. When cool, transfer the solution to a Petri dish or watch glass. Leave it for a few days to allow the water to evaporate. *Step F*

9. Observe the shape and colour of the copper sulfate crystals formed.

Practical Objective

To prepare a sample of pure, dry, hydrated copper sulfate crystals from copper oxide.

Content Objective

Soluble salts can be made by reacting acids with metals, metal oxides, hydroxides or carbonates to produce a solution of the salt, which can be crystallised to produce a solid salt.

Apparatus

- safety goggles
- 250 cm³ beaker
- 100 cm³ beakers
- Bunsen burner
- gauze and tripod
- heatproof mat
- Petri dish or watch glass
- 100 cm³ measuring cylinder
- evaporating basin
- spatula
- stirring rod
- filter funnel
- filter paper
- tongs
- dilute sulfuric acid
- copper(II) oxide

Safety ⚠

- Wear safety goggles at all times.
- Care is needed with hot acid.
- Never heat to dryness.

Recording your results

1   Describe the colour, shape and size of the copper sulfate crystals produced.

2   Describe the appearance of:

a   the sulfuric acid

b   the copper oxide

c   the solution at the end of the reaction.

Considering your results

3   Write a word equation to show the reaction you have carried out.

4   Give a reason why you need to be sure excess copper oxide is added in step **D**.

5   Name the substance left in the filter paper in step **E**.

6   What is dissolved in the solution that went through the filter paper?

7   Explain why this is an example of a neutralisation reaction.

8   What substance acts as a base in this reaction?

9   Write a symbol equation to show the reaction you have carried out. Include the state symbols.
       Use your answer to question **3** to help you.

Exam-style questions

1 The reaction between copper carbonate and dilute hydrochloric acid produces copper chloride, water and carbon dioxide.

1.1 Explain why safety goggles are worn to protect the eyes when carrying out this reaction. **[1 mark]**

_____
_____

1.2 Write a balanced equation for this reaction. **[2 marks]**

_____
_____
_____

1.3 Using this reaction, describe a method to make pure, dry crystals of copper chloride. **[4 marks]**

_____
_____
_____
_____
_____
_____
_____
_____
_____
_____
_____
_____
_____

The electrolysis of molten or dissolved ionic salts is carried out using inert (unreactive) electrodes (usually graphite or platinum). When a molten salt is electrolysed, ions are discharged as atoms or molecules at the electrodes. However, electrolysis of dissolved ionic salts is more complex. This is because water ionises to a very small extent, so in an aqueous solution of a salt there are some hydrogen ions (H^+) and hydroxide ions (OH^-), as well as the ions of the dissolved solid. You are going to predict the substances formed at electrodes when different substances are electrolysed. You will then carry out the electrolysis of these substances to confirm whether you were right.

Your teacher may watch to see if you can:

- follow instructions carefully
- work safely.

Core learning outcomes: I am able to…
use appropriate apparatus and techniques for conducting and monitoring chemical reactions
use appropriate apparatus and techniques to draw, set up and use electrochemical cells for separation and production of elements and compounds
use appropriate qualitative reagents and techniques to analyse and identify unknown samples or products including gas tests for hydrogen, oxygen and chlorine.

Hypothesis

Write down your hypothesis. Explain why you made this hypothesis.

_____

_____

_____

_____

_____

_____

_____

_____

_____

Practical Objective ▶

To investigate the substances that are formed at the electrode: when different salt solutions are electrolysed.

Content Objective ▶

Predict the products of the electrolysis of aqueous solutions containing a single ionic compound.

Apparatus ▶

- safety goggles
- copper(II) sulfate solution
- sodium chloride solution
- carbon electrodes
- 100 cm³ beaker
- Petri dish lid
- tweezers
- connecting leads
- copper(II) chloride solution
- sodium sulfate solution
- low voltage power supply
- damp litmus paper
- electrode holder

Safety ⚠

- Safety goggles need to be worn throughout the practica

Prediction

Now that you have studied electrolysis, predict what products will be formed at each electrode and give reasons for your predictions.

Solution	Positive electrode	Negative electrode	Why I think...
copper(II) chloride			(positive electrode)
			(negative electrode)
copper(II) sulfate			(positive electrode)
			(negative electrode)
sodium chloride			(positive electrode)
			(negative electrode)
sodium sulfate			(positive electrode)
			(negative electrode)

Method

A Place about 50 cm³ of copper(II) chloride solution into a 100 cm³ beaker.

B Insert the carbon electrodes into the electrode holder and place this into the copper(II) chloride solution.

C Use the leads to connect the electrodes to the low voltage power supply. Make sure you connect the electrodes to the d.c. terminals. These are normally coloured red and black.

D Set the voltage to 6 V and switch on.

E Look at the electrodes. Write any observations in the results table. There could be a colour change or fizzing.

F Hold a piece of damp litmus paper close to the electrode that is bubbling. (This should be the positive electrode.) What do you see happening? Add this information to your results table on the next page.

G After a few minutes, switch off the low voltage supply and take a closer look at the other electrode. (This should be the negative electrode.) Is there a colour change? Record any information in your results table.

H Remove the liquid from the beaker. Your teacher will tell you where to put this. You will need to clean both electrodes. Rinsing them under running water should be fine.

Repeat steps **A** to **H** using the other solutions.

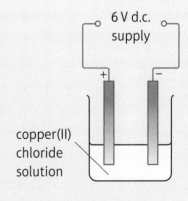

6 V d.c. supply

copper(II) chloride solution

Considering your results/conclusions

1   Make sure your table below is complete. Remember to write in your evidence.

Solution	Positive electrode	Negative electrode	Evidence for this...
copper(II) chloride			(positive electrode)
			(negative electrode)
copper(II) sulfate			(positive electrode)
			(negative electrode)
sodium chloride			(positive electrode)
			(negative electrode)
sodium sulfate			(positive electrode)
			(negative electrode)

2   Compare your final results with the predictions you made at the start. How accurate were your predictions?

3   The test for chlorine is that it bleaches damp litmus paper. The other two gases you are likely to have found wou need additional tests to confirm what they are. Write down the names of these gases and the tests for them.

Exam-style questions

1 Aqueous solutions can be electrolysed using inert electrodes.

1.1 Complete the table below to show the substances formed at the electrodes. **[2 marks]**

| | Substance formed | |
Aqueous solution	Negative electrode	Positive electrode
magnesium chloride solution		
copper sulfate solution		

1.2 Explain your answers for the negative electrodes. **[2 marks]**

Magnesium chloride solution: _____
_____

Copper sulfate solution: _____
_____

1.3 Using the space below, now give the tests for the following gases: **[3 marks]**

Oxygen: _____
_____

Hydrogen: _____
_____

Chlorine: _____
_____

1.4 Copper can be purified by electrolysis. Pure copper is deposited at the negative electrode.

Write the half equation for the reaction at the negative electrode. **[2 marks]**

_____

During a chemical reaction, energy is transferred between the reacting substances and their surroundings. This energy transfer is usually by heating, particularly if a reaction takes place in solution. The stored thermal (heat) energy in the solution increases during an exothermic reaction, and decreases during an endothermic reaction. This means you can determine whether a reaction in solution is exothermic or endothermic:

- the temperature of the solution increases in an exothermic reaction
- the temperature of the solution decreases in an endothermic reaction.

You are going to investigate a type of reaction known as a neutralisation reaction.

Your teacher may watch to see if you can:

- follow instructions carefully
- work safely.

Core learning outcomes: I am able to…
use appropriate apparatus to make and record a range of measurements accurately, including mass, temperature and volume of liquids
use appropriate apparatus and techniques for conducting and monitoring chemical reactions
make and record appropriate observations during chemical reactions, including changes in temperature
safely use and carefully handle gases, liquids and solids, including carefully mixing reagents under controlled conditions and using appropriate apparatus to explore chemical changes.

Practical Objective

To react hydrochloric acid with sodium hydroxide solution in a neutralisation reaction and measure the temperature change

Content Objective

Distinguish between exothermic and endothermic reactions. Investigate the variables that affect temperature changes in reacting solutions such as acids plus metals or carbonates, neutralisations, and displacemen of metals.

Apparatus

- eye protection
- safety goggles
- two polystyrene cups
- 250 cm³ beaker
- lid for one cup
- measuring cylinders
- sodium hydroxide
- hydrochloric acid
- tripod
- thermometer

Hypothesis

Write down your hypothesis for this experiment. You could also include a sketch graph.

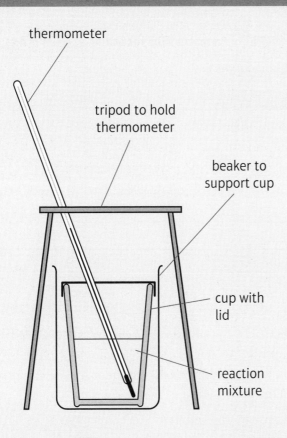

thermometer

tripod to hold
thermometer

beaker to
support cup

cup with
lid

reaction
mixture

Safety

- Wear safety goggles.
- Sodium hydroxide and hydrochloric acid at this concentration are corrosive and very damaging to eyes.

Method

Use a measuring cylinder to put 30 cm³ of 2.0 mol/dm³ hydrochloric acid into a polystyrene cup.

Clean out the measuring cylinder with water.

Place the polystyrene cup into a glass beaker to make it more stable. Measure the temperature of the acid and write this in your results table. This should go in the column for Experiment 1.

Use the measuring cylinder to put 40 cm³ of 2.0 mol/dm³ sodium hydroxide solution into a second polystyrene cup.

Remove 5 cm³ of 2.0 mol/dm³ sodium hydroxide solution from the 40 cm³ of solution measured out in step **D**.

Add this to the polystyrene cup containing the acid. Put the lid on the cup containing the mixture and stir it using the thermometer. Enclose the thermometer with a tripod to stop the cup and thermometer tipping over.

Keep stirring until the temperature reaches a maximum and starts to fall. Record the highest temperature in your table.

Repeat steps **E** to **G** until all of the 40 cm³ of sodium hydroxide solution has been added.

When you have finished, rinse out your cups and measuring cylinders and repeat the experiment at least one more time. If time is short, you could use results from other groups because everyone will have used the same amounts and the same strengths of solutions.

Considering your results/conclusions

Record your results in the table on the following page. There are some extra columns for repeated results from your experiments or results from other groups. To calculate the mean, add up all of the results in a row and divide by the number of results in the row.

Volume of sodium hydroxide solution added in cm³	Maximum temperature recorded at each stage in °C				
	Experiment 1	**Experiment 2**			**Mean**
0					
5					
10					
15					
20					
25					
30					
35					
40					

2 On the next page, draw a graph of your results with the volume of sodium hydroxide solution added in cm³ (the independent variable) on the *x*-axis and the mean maximum temperature in °C (the dependent variable) on the *y*-axis.

3 Draw two straight lines of best fit. One will be through all the points which are increasing in temperature and the other will be through all the points which are decreasing in temperature. You need to make sure the lines cross, so you might need to extend them. The diagram on the right should give you an idea of what this should look like.

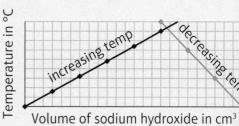

4 What volumes of hydrochloric acid and sodium hydroxide would produce the largest temperature rise?

5 Why does the temperature start to fall towards the end of the experiment?

Evaluation

6 How could you make the data you collect from this investigation more accurate?

It is difficult to find the exact volume of sodium hydroxide solution that would give the maximum temperature rise. What further work would you need to carry out to find this exact volume of sodium hydroxide?

_____

_____

Exam-style questions

01   The reaction between solid citric acid and sodium hydrogencarbonate solution produces a temperature change.

A student investigates the effect of changing the mass of citric acid on the temperature change.

Mass of citric acid in g	Starting temperature in °C	Temperature in °C after 1 minute
3.4	21.0	18.3
5.5	21.6	17.2

01.1   Give **one** control variable for this investigation.   **[1 mark]**

_____

_____

01.2 The student concluded that the mass of citric acid makes no difference in this reaction.
Give **one** reason why the student cannot make this conclusion from these results. **[1 ma**

01.3 Explain a conclusion that can be made about the reaction from these results. **[2 mar**

01.4 Another student measures the temperature change differently. The student produces this graph using 4.0 g o
citric acid.
Label the independent variable on the graph. **[1 ma**

01.5 Explain **two** reasons why the student might have stopped measuring at 60 seconds. **[2 mark**

01.6 Predict a more valid temperature value at 60 seconds. **[1 mar**

The progress of a chemical reaction can be measured by how the amounts of reactant or product change with time, or by the time taken for the reaction to reach a certain point.

You are going to investigate the reaction between hydrochloric acid and marble chips (calcium carbonate) to find out how the concentration of the acid affects the rate. You will monitor the progress of the reaction by measuring the volume of carbon dioxide produced.

Core learning outcomes: I am able to…

| use appropriate apparatus to make and record a range of measurements accurately, including mass, temperature, and volume of liquids |
| use appropriate apparatus and techniques for conducting and monitoring chemical reactions |
| make and record appropriate observations during chemical reactions including changes in temperature |
| safely use and carefully handle gases, liquids and solids, including carefully mixing reagents under controlled conditions, using appropriate apparatus to explore chemical changes. |

Part 1: Measuring gas production

Your teacher may watch to see if you can:

- carefully control variables during investigations
- measure change accurately.

Hypothesis

Write down your hypothesis. Explain your hypothesis.

_____

_____

_____

_____

_____

_____

_____

Practical Objective

To investigate the effect on the rate of reaction of changing the concentration of solutions by measuring the production of a gas.

Content Objective

Factors which affect the rates of chemical reactions include the concentrations of reactants in solution, the pressure of reacting gases, the surface area of solid reactants, the temperature and the presence of catalysts.

Apparatus

- eye protection
- balance
- water trough
- 100 cm³ measuring cylinder
- stop clock
- conical flask
- delivery tube and bung
- marble chips
- 1.0 mol/dm³ and 1.5 mol/dm³ hydrochloric acid

Safety

- Wear eye protection at all times.
- Care is needed with acid solutions. Wash off splashes immediately.

Method

. Set up the apparatus as shown in the diagram.

. Measure 20 cm³ of 1.0 mol/dm³ hydrochloric acid into a conical flask.

. Add 5 g of marble chips to the flask (three or four pieces of equal size).

. Wait briefly, then stopper the flask and start the stop clock.

. Note the total volume of gas produced after every 30 seconds for five minutes or until the reaction has finished.

. Repeat steps **A** to **E** using 1.5 mol/dm³ hydrochloric acid.

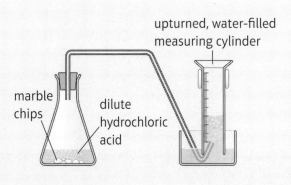

marble chips · dilute hydrochloric acid · upturned, water-filled measuring cylinder

Recording your results

1 Record your results in the table below.

Time (min)	0	0.5	1.0	1.5	2.0	2.5	3.0	3.5	4.0	4.5	5.0
Volume of gas produced using 1.0 mol/dm³ hydrochloric acid (cm³)											
Volume of gas produced using 1.5 mol/dm³ hydrochloric acid (cm³)											

Considering your results/conclusion

2 Plot the points for both sets of results on the same graph. The volume of gas produced in cm³ (the dependent variable) should be on the *y*-axis. The time in minutes (the independent variable) should be on the *x*-axis. Use different coloured lines for the two concentrations of acid.

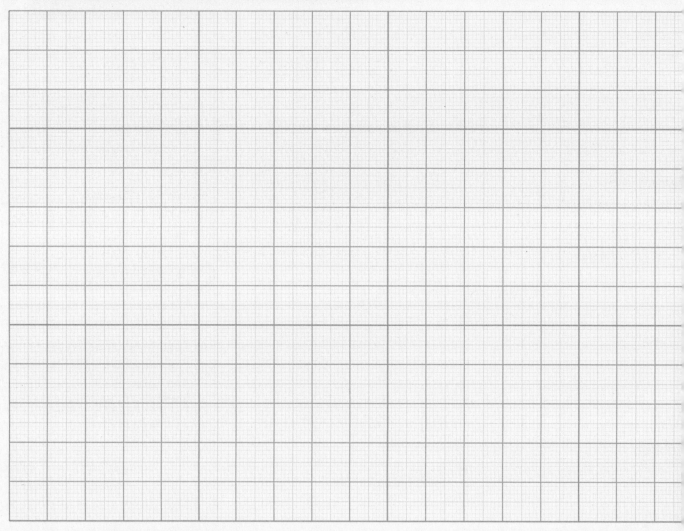

Explain how you can tell from the graphs when the reactions were finished.

_____

_____

_____

Describe how increasing the concentration affects the rate of reaction.

_____

_____

Explain how your results and graphs fit with your conclusion in question **4**.

_____

_____

_____

_____

Evaluation

Suggest possible sources of error in this investigation.

_____

_____

_____

_____

Suggest possible changes to the method that could improve the reliability of the results.

_____

_____

_____

_____

AQA GCSE (9–1)
Combined science
Practical 11: Rates of reaction
(Part 2: Observing a colour chang

Part 2: Observing a colour change

The progress of a chemical reaction can be measured by how amounts of reactant or product change with time, or by the time taken for the reaction to reach a certain point.

You are going to investigate the effect of concentration on the rate of reaction between sodium thiosulfate and hydrochloric acid. You will monitor the progress of the reaction by observing a colour change.

Your teacher may watch to see if you can:

- carefully control variables during investigations
- measure change accurately
- work safely.

Hypothesis

Write down your hypothesis. Explain your hypothesis.

_____

_____

_____

_____

_____

_____

Method

A Place $10\,cm^3$ of sodium thiosulfate solution and $40\,cm^3$ of water into a $250\,cm^3$ conical flask.

B Measure $10\,cm^3$ of dilute hydrochloric acid into a measuring cylinder.

C Place the conical flask (containing the previously measured out sodium thiosulfate and water) on a piece of white paper marked with a cross, as shown opposite.

D Add the acid to the thiosulfate and start the stop clock.

E Looking down from above, stop the clock when the cross disappears.

F Note this time.

G Repeat steps **A** to **F** four times, but each time change the volumes of sodium thiosulfate and water in step **A** as follows:
- $20\,cm^3$ sodium thiosulfate + $30\,cm^3$ water
- $30\,cm^3$ sodium thiosulfate + $20\,cm^3$ water
- $40\,cm^3$ sodium thiosulfate + $10\,cm^3$ water
- $50\,cm^3$ sodium thiosulfate + no water

H If time is short, your teacher may suggest that you share results with other groups instead.

Practical Objective

To investigate the effect of changing the concentration on the rate of reaction between sodium thiosulfate and hydrochloric acid, by observing a colour change in the solutions.

Content Objective

Factors which affect the rates of chemical reactions include the concentrations of reactants in solution, the pressure of reacting gases, the surface area of solid reactants, the temperature and the presence of catalysts.

Apparatus

- eye protection
- $250\,cm^3$ conical flask
- $10\,cm^3$ measuring cylinder
- $50\,cm^3$ measuring cylinder
- stop clock
- test tube
- test-tube rack
- white paper with cross
- sodium thiosulfate solution
- dilute hydrochloric acid

Safety

- Wear eye protection at all times.
- Care is needed with acid solutions. Wash off splashes immediately.
- Take care to avoid breathing in any sulfur dioxide fumes.

Recording your results

1 Record your results in the table below. The final column has the concentrations of sodium thiosulfate worked out for you (providing you used the suggested amounts of water and sodium thiosulfate). This will help you with later questions.

Volume of sodium thiosulfate (cm³)	Volume of water (cm³)	Time taken for cross to disappear from view (seconds)				Concentration of sodium thiosulfate (g/dm³)
		Experiment 1	Experiment 2	Experiment 3	Mean	
10	40					8
20	30					16
30	20					24
40	10					32
50	0					40

Considering your results/conclusion

2 Plot a graph with mean time taken for the cross to disappear from view, in seconds (the dependent variable) on the y-axis and sodium thiosulfate concentration in g/dm³ (the independent variable) on the x-axis. Draw a smooth curved line of best fit.

3 **a** Describe how concentration affects the rate of this reaction.

b Explain your answer to part **a** by referring to the shape of your graph.

4 If the rate of reaction doubled, what would happen to the time taken for the cross to disappear?

5 Compare your results with other groups. How similar are they? Does this mean the investigation is reproducible?

Compare your results from Parts 1 and 2. Both investigations looked at the effect of changing concentration, using different methods to measure the rate of reaction.
Can you see a similar pattern in both investigations?

_____
_____
_____
_____
_____
_____
_____
_____
_____

Evaluation

Describe **two** possible sources of error in this investigation.

_____
_____
_____
_____

Suggest a way of reducing one of these errors.

_____
_____
_____
_____

Exam-style questions

01.1 The reaction between calcium carbonate and dilute hydrochloric acid produces a gas.
Complete the word equation for the reaction. **[2 marks]**

Calcium carbonate + hydrochloric acid → _____

01.2 A student investigates the rate of this reaction. They collect the gas in a measuring cylinder.
Explain why they do not collect the gas in a test tube. **[2 marks]**

01.3 Suggest an alternative piece of equipment for collecting the gas. **[1 mark]**

01.4 The student investigates the effect of changing the surface area of the calcium carbonate.
Name **two** control variables. **[2 marks]**

01.5 The student measures the volume of gas collected every 30 seconds until the reaction is finished.
Predict the shapes of the graphs for calcium carbonate powder and calcium carbonate chips. Draw both graphs on the same axes and include all labels. **[4 marks]**

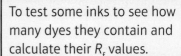

Many inks contain a mixture of dyes. Chromatography can be used to identify inks; for example, inks from crime scenes or from documents that may have been forged. You are going to carry out an experiment using paper chromatography. You will then use the results to calculate R_f values.

Your teacher may watch to see if you can:

- follow instructions carefully
- draw conclusions from your results.

Core learning outcomes: I am able to...

- use appropriate apparatus to make and record a range of measurements accurately
- safely use a range of equipment to purify and/or separate chemical mixtures, including chromatography.

Method

A. Check that your chromatography paper hangs close to the bottom of the empty beaker without touching it (as shown in the diagram).

B. Take the paper out of the beaker and draw a pencil line on the paper, about 2 cm from the bottom.

C. Put a small spot of ink from each pen on your pencil line.

D. Write the name of each pen or ink below each spot with a pencil.

E. Pour some water into the beaker to a depth of about 1 cm.

F. Lower the chromatography paper into the beaker so that the bottom of the paper is in the water, but the water level is below the spots (see the diagram).

G. Leave the paper in the beaker until the water has soaked up the paper almost to the top. The water is the solvent for the different coloured dye compounds in the inks. The solvent is called the mobile phase in chromatography, because it is the part that moves.

H. Take the paper out and immediately use a pencil to mark the location of the solvent front (the level the water reached) before it evaporates. Leave the paper to dry.

Practical Objective

To test some inks to see how many dyes they contain and calculate their R_f values.

Content Objective

Paper chromatography can be used to separate mixtures. The R_f value is the ratio of the distance moved by a compound to the distance moved by the solvent.

Apparatus

- pencil and ruler
- beaker
- chromatography paper attached to a pencil, rod or splint
- two marker pens or felt-tip pens

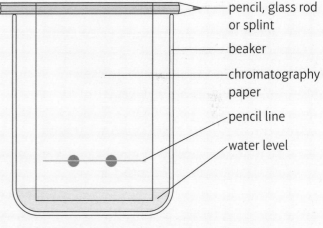

pencil, glass rod or splint

beaker

chromatography paper

pencil line

water level

Recording your results

1 Describe the results for each pen on the chromatogram.

2 Measure the distance the solvent (the water) has risen from the pencil line.

3 Measure the distance that each dye spot has risen from the pencil line (i.e. measure from the pencil line to the top of each different coloured spot). Write your results in the tables below.

Name of pen/ink:				
Colours of dye spots				
Distance of spot from pencil line (cm)				
R_f value (see below for formula)				

Name of pen/ink:				
Colours of dye spots				
Distance of spot from pencil line (cm)				
R_f value (see below for formula)				

Considering your results/conclusions

4 Use the formula below to calculate the R_f value for each separate colour in the two inks. Add these values to the tables above.

$$R_f = \frac{\text{distance moved by the coloured spot}}{\text{distance moved by the solvent}}$$

5 Were any of the inks a pure colour? Explain your conclusion.

6 Did the same coloured dyes appear in more than one ink?
    If so, do you think they were the same chemical compound? Explain your answer.

Evaluation

7 Why was the starting line drawn in pencil?

_____

_____

_____

_____

8 Why did you have to label the spots?

_____

_____

9 Why is the chromatography paper hung with the bottom just in the water?

_____

_____

Exam-style questions

01.1 Explain how paper chromatography separates mixtures. **[3 marks]**

01.2 Explain why calculating the R_f value can allow a compound to be identified. **[2 marks]**

01.3 The diagram below shows a chromatogram of four different food colourings.

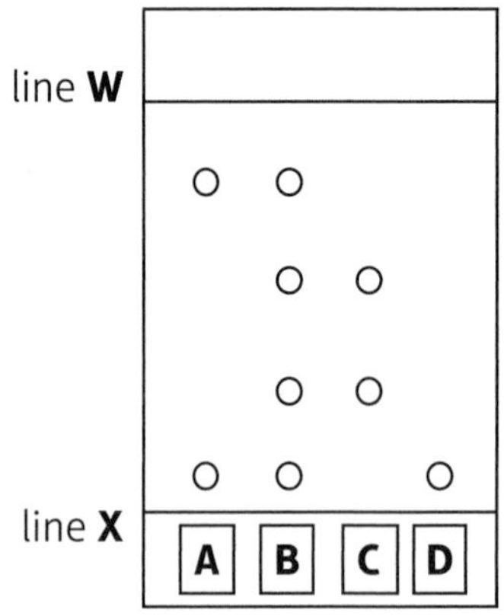

What is shown by line **W**? **[1 mark]**

01.4 Identify which food colouring is a mixture of **two** of the others. **[1 mark]**

Food colouring

01.5 Give **two** other conclusions about the food colourings that can be made from the chromatogram. **[2 marks]**

1.6 Calculate the R_f for food colouring **D**. Write down the equation you will use.

Give your answer to two significant figures. **[3 marks]**

R_f value =

Water is one of our most valuable raw materials. It is used in washing and cleaning as well as agriculture and industry. Probably its most important use is for drinking. Around the world, there is a need to ensure that water provided is fit to drink. This is known as potable water. In your investigation, you will test a sample of water before and after distilling it to see if you have managed to produce potable water.

Your teacher may watch to see if you can:

- follow instructions carefully
- work safely.

Core learning outcomes: I am able to…
safely use appropriate heating devices and techniques including a Bunsen burner, water bath or electric heater
use appropriate apparatus and techniques for the measurement of pH in different situations
safely use a range of equipment to purify and/or separate chemical mixtures including evaporation, distillation.

Method 1: Pre-distillation and post-distillation

A Put about 1 cm depth of salty water into a test tube.

Flame test (metal ions)

B Carry out a flame test on this sample by dipping the nichrome wire into the sample and holding it in a blue Bunsen burner flame. The flame colour will indicate which substance (positive metal ion) is present in the sample. Record your results in the table on the following page.

Possible flame colours: **yellow** – sodium, **lilac** – potassium, **crimson** – lithium, **brick red** – calcium, **green** – barium

Nitric acid/Silver nitrate test (halide ions)

C Add 3–4 drops of dilute nitric acid to the remaining salty water sample in the test tube. Then add 1 cm depth of silver nitrate solution. The colour of the precipitate will indicate which substance (negative halide ion) is present in the sample. Record your results in the table on the following page.

Possible precipitate colours: **white –** chloride ions, **cream** – bromide ions, **yellow** – iodide ions

D Clean out the test tube and move on to Method 2: Distillation.

Practical Objective

To produce potable water from a provided salty water sample and to complete tests on the water sample before and after distillation to prove it is now pure water.

Content Objective

Salty water can be desalinated by distillation. The presence of ions in the water before and afte distillation can be tested.

Apparatus

- eye protection
- salty water sample
- dilute nitric acid
- silver nitrate solution
- nichrome wire
- Bunsen burner
- heat-resistant mat
- test tubes

Safety

- Wear eye protection.

Method 2: Distillation

A Set up your apparatus as shown in the diagram. Clamp the conical flask to hold it securely. Put anti-bumping granules in the bottom of the flask.

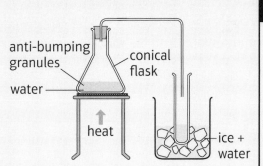

F Adjust the Bunsen burner so you have a gentle blue flame. The air hole should be about half open and the gas tap should be about half on. Heat the water until it boils.

G Collect the distillate in the test tube. Try to collect approximately the same amount as the original amount you tested in step **A**.

H Repeat steps **A** to **D** on this newly distilled sample of water.

Apparatus

- eye protection
- salty water sample
- ice
- 250 cm³ beaker
- 250 cm³ conical flask
- clamp and stand
- anti-bumping granules
- Bunsen burner
- tripod
- heat-resistant mat
- gauze
- delivery tube with bung

Safety ⚠

- Wear eye protection.
- Tie long hair back.

Considering your results/conclusions

Write your results in the table below.
(Hint: Remember what results you should have obtained if using a sample of 'salty water', i.e. sodium chloride solution.)

	Sample	Flame test (positive metal ions)	Nitric acid/silver nitrate test (negative halide ions)
Before	Salty water		
After	Distilled water		

Did you purify the water successfully? Explain your answer.

_____

_____

_____

What other test could you carry out to show that the newly distilled sample is water?

_____

_____

Evaluation

4 Explain what happened when the salty water was distilled. In your explanation, use the following words: boil, evaporate, liquid, steam, temperature, vapour. Continue your answer on a separate sheet of paper if you need to.

Exam-style questions

01.1 The table below gives the pH value of three solutions.

Write a conclusion for each solution shown in the table, to identify whether it is acidic, alkaline or neutral. State the strength in each case. **[2 mark**

Solution	pH value	Conclusion
A	6.4	
B	12.5	
C	7.0	

01.2 Give **two** ways that the pH of a solution can be measured. **[2 mark**

01.3 Compare the advantages and disadvantages of using the **two** ways of measuring the pH of a solution. **[3 mark**

1.4 Explain how simple distillation can be used to produce potable water from a solution.   **[2 marks]**

65

1.5 Describe how to test the water to confirm that any metal ions have been removed by distillation.   **[3 marks]**

The specific heat capacity of a substance is the energy needed to raise the temperature of 1 kg of the substance by 1 °C. The unit of specific heat capacity is the joule per kilogram per degree Celsius (J/kg °C). You are going to calculate the specific heat capacity of a metal block and compare your findings with published results.

Your teacher may watch to see if you can:

- follow instructions carefully
- work safely.

Core learning outcomes: I am able to…

use appropriate apparatus to make and record measurements of mass, time and temperature accurately

use, in a safe manner, appropriate apparatus to measure energy changes/ transfers and associated values such as work done.

Method

A Obtain your metal block, make a note of the metal you have been given and measure its mass in kg, using a top pan balance.

B Put the immersion heater in the large hole and connect it as shown in the diagram to the right. Ask your teacher to check your connections.

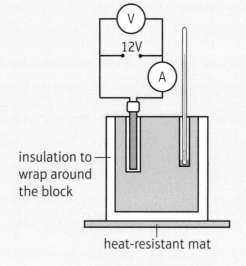

insulation to wrap around the block

heat-resistant mat

C Ensure the power supply is set to 12 V. Record the initial temperature using the thermometer. NB You **must** record the initial temperature before switching on.

D Start the stop clock as you switch on the power supply and make a note of the readings on the two meters. The readings should remain constant. Check at the end that the meter readings are still approximately the same.

E Record the temperature every minute for the next 10 minutes.

F The power of the immersion heater can be calculated from the current (A) that flows through it and the potenti difference (V) across it.

Calculate the power using the equation: $P = I \times V$

P is the power in watts, W

I is the current in amperes (amps), A

V is the potential difference in volts, V

Block material	Block mass (kg)	Current (A)	Potential difference (V)	Power of the heater (W)

Practical Objective

To measure the specific heat capacity of a metal block.

Content Objective

Specific heat capacity is the amount of energy required to raise the temperature of 1 kg of substance by 1 °C.

Apparatus

- 1 kg blocks of copper, iron and aluminium
- insulation to wrap around the blocks
- immersion heater and powe supply
- heat-resistant mat
- thermometer
- stop clock
- connecting wires
- balance
- ammeter
- voltmeter

Safety

- Take care as the heaters and blocks will get hot enough to burn your skin.

Considering your results/conclusions

Record your temperature measurements in the table below.

Time (seconds)	Temperature (°C)	Work done by the heater (J)
0		
60		
120		
180		
240		
300		
360		
420		
480		
540		
600		

Complete the last column in your table. Since power (P) = work done (W) / time (t), to calculate the work done by the heater you will need to multiply the power value of the heater (worked out in step **F**) by the time (in seconds).

On the next page, draw a graph of your results. You need to put work done by the heater on the x-axis and temperature on the y-axis. You need to add a line of best fit.

Find the straightest part of your graph and work out the gradient. Then use the following equation to work out the heat capacity of the block:

$$\frac{1}{gradient} = \text{heat capacity of the block}$$

Work done = thermal energy supplied = heat capacity × change in temperature

(since heat capacity = mass × specific heat capacity)

So work done/change in temperature = heat capacity = 1/gradient

Use this value to calculate the specific heat capacity of the material of the block, using the following equation:

$$\frac{\text{heat capacity of the block}}{\text{mass of the block (kg)}} = \text{specific heat capacity of the block}$$

Evaluation

6 If you have not had sufficient time to complete the experiment with all three metal blocks yourself, share result from other groups. Then compare your results with the accepted published values for specific heat capacity of t different metals. How do your results compare? Explain why they might not be exactly the same.

Block material	Specific heat capacity in joules per kilogram per degree Celsius (J/kg/°C)
Aluminium	913
Copper	385
Iron	500

xam-style questions

1.1 A student wants to find the specific heat capacity of copper. Identify the apparatus the student should use. **[3 marks]**

_____

_____

_____

_____

1.2 Draw a labelled diagram showing how the apparatus should be assembled. **[3 marks]**

1.3 Describe the method the student should use to determine the specific heat capacity of copper.

Your account should include reference to:

- The measurements the student needs to make, the instruments that could be used to take those measurements and the resolution of those instruments.
- How would the student use the measurements to calculate the specific heat capacity?
- How will the student ensure results are valid?
- Any safety considerations that should be taken into account. **[6 marks]**

_____

_____

_____

_____

_____

_____

_____

(*Continue answer on next page.*)

01.4   Explain why specific heat capacity results found in a school laboratory are often quite inaccurate.   **[2 mar**

01.5   Calculate the specific heat capacity of a 1 kg block of copper if 7720 J of energy supplied causes the temperature of the block to rise from 20 °C to 40 °C. Include the unit in your answer.   **[3 mar**

Some wires and components need a larger potential difference to produce a current through them than others. This is because they have a large electrical resistance. Resistance is measured in units called ohms (Ω). The resistance of a wire, a component or a circuit is calculated using the equation:

potential difference = current × resistance
(V)   (A)   (Ω)

First you will investigate how resistance is affected by the length of a wire. In the second experiment, you will look at resistors in series and in parallel.

Your teacher may watch to see if you can:

- follow instructions carefully
- work safely.

Core learning outcomes: I am able to…

use appropriate apparatus to measure and record length accurately
use appropriate apparatus to measure current, potential difference and resistance
use circuit diagrams to construct and check series and parallel circuits.

Part 1: To investigate how the length of a wire affects its resistance

Hypothesis

Write down a hypothesis for this experiment.

_____

_____

_____

Method

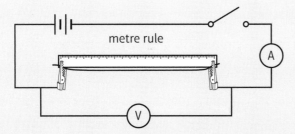
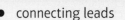

A Set up the circuit as shown in the diagram above. The metre rule should already have a piece of wire attached along its length. The switch which is shown in the circuit is the switch on the low voltage power supply. Set the low voltage power supply to 6 V.

B Make sure one crocodile clip is at one end of the metre rule, connected to the wire being tested.

C Clip the second crocodile clip to the wire level with the 20 cm mark. Switch on the power supply. Record the ammeter and voltmeter readings in the table below. Switch off the power supply as soon as you have taken the readings. Do not leave the power on for more than a few seconds.

D Move the second crocodile clip along the wire so a longer length of wire is used. Repeat steps **A** to **D** for four more different lengths, up to 1 metre.

Apparatus

- connecting leads
- low voltage power supply
- wire to be tested, attached to a metre rule
- crocodile clips
- ammeter
- voltmeter

Safety

- Take care as short lengths of wire can get hot. Switch off the power supply between readings. Only switch on power for a few seconds at a time.
- Ask your teacher to check your circuit before you switch it on.

Considering your results/conclusions

1   Write your results in the table below.

Length of wire being tested (cm)				
Current (A)				
Potential difference (V)				
Resistance (Ω) (see equation below)				

2   Calculate resistance for the bottom row using the following equation:

$$\text{resistance } (\Omega) = \frac{\text{potential difference (V)}}{\text{current (A)}}$$

3   On the graph paper below, draw a graph of resistance against length of wire being tested. The resistance (dependent variable) should go on the *y*-axis and the length of wire being tested (independent variable) should go on the *x*-axis. Draw a straight line of best fit.

4   What conclusion can you draw from your results and graph? Was your hypothesis correct?

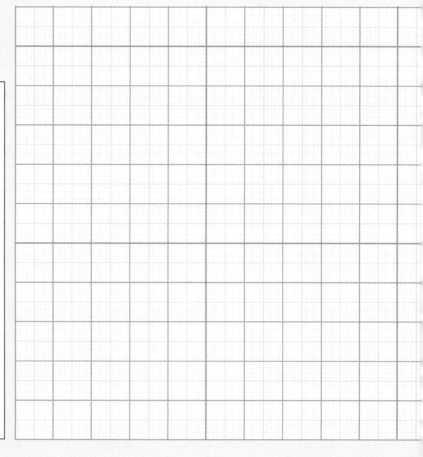

5   Use evidence from your graph and your calculations to explain how you came to your conclusion.

Evaluation

Look at your graph.

a Does the line of best fit go through the origin? If it does go through the origin, what does this show? If it does not, suggest a reason why.

_____

_____

b How close were your points to the line of best fit? What does this tell you about the quality of your data?

_____

_____

How reproducible were your results? (Hint: Compare your results with other groups.)

_____

_____

Name one systematic error and one random error which could occur in this experiment.

Systematic _____

Random _____

Part 2: Resistors in series and parallel

Hypothesis

Write down a hypothesis for this experiment.

_____

_____

_____

_____

Apparatus

- connecting leads
- low voltage power supply
- two 10 Ω resistors
- ammeter
- voltmeter

Safety

- Ask your teacher to check your circuit before you switch it on.

Method

Test 1: One resistor

A Set up the circuit as shown in the diagram on the right.

B Switch on the power supply and record the current using the ammeter, and the potential difference using the voltmeter. Then switch off the power.

C Calculate the total resistance for the circuit using the equation:

$$\text{resistance } (\Omega) = \frac{\text{potential difference (V)}}{\text{current (A)}}$$

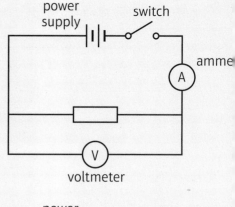

Current (A)	Potential difference (V)	Resistance (Ω)

Test 2: Two resistors in series

D Set up the circuit as shown in the diagram on the right.

E Switch on the power supply and record the current and potential difference. Then switch off the power.

F Calculate the total resistance for the circuit using the equation above:

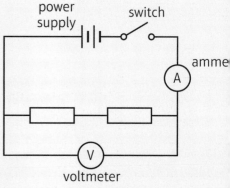

Current (A)	Potential difference (V)	Resistance (Ω)

Test 3: Two resistors in parallel

G Set up the circuit as shown in the diagram on the right.

H Switch on the power supply and record the current and potential difference. Then switch off the power.

I Calculate the total resistance for the circuit using the equation above.

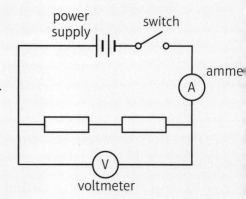

Current (A)	Potential difference (V)	Resistance (Ω)

Considering your results/conclusions

1 Look at the resistance values you worked out in the three tests.
What is the effect on the total resistance in a circuit of adding another resistor in series? (Hint: Compare your results for Test 1 and Test 2.)

2 What is the effect on the total resistance in a circuit of adding another resistor in parallel? (Hint: Compare your results for Test 1 and Test 3.)

What conclusions can be made about resistors in series and resistors in parallel in electrical circuits? Was your hypothesis correct?

Based on your results, predict what would happen if you added:

a a third resistor in series

b a third resistor in parallel?

Exam-style questions

1.1 A student investigated how length affects the resistance of a wire.

Draw a labelled circuit that would be suitable for the student to use. **[3 marks]**

Some of the student's results are shown in the table below.

Length (m)	Resistance (Ω)			
	Test 1	**Test 2**	**Test 3**	**Mean**
0.15	0.80	0.90	1.00	0.90
0.25	1.45	1.55	1.50	1.50
0.45	2.70	2.90	2.80	
0.55		3.50	3.65	3.50
0.75	5.08	5.00		5.00
0.95	6.45	6.30	6.15	6.30

1.2 Complete the table by calculating the missing values. **[3 marks]**

01.3 Explain which length of wire has the most precise resistance readings. **[2 mar**

01.4 Why did the student do three tests and calculate a mean? **[2 mar**

The student plotted all their points on the graph below.

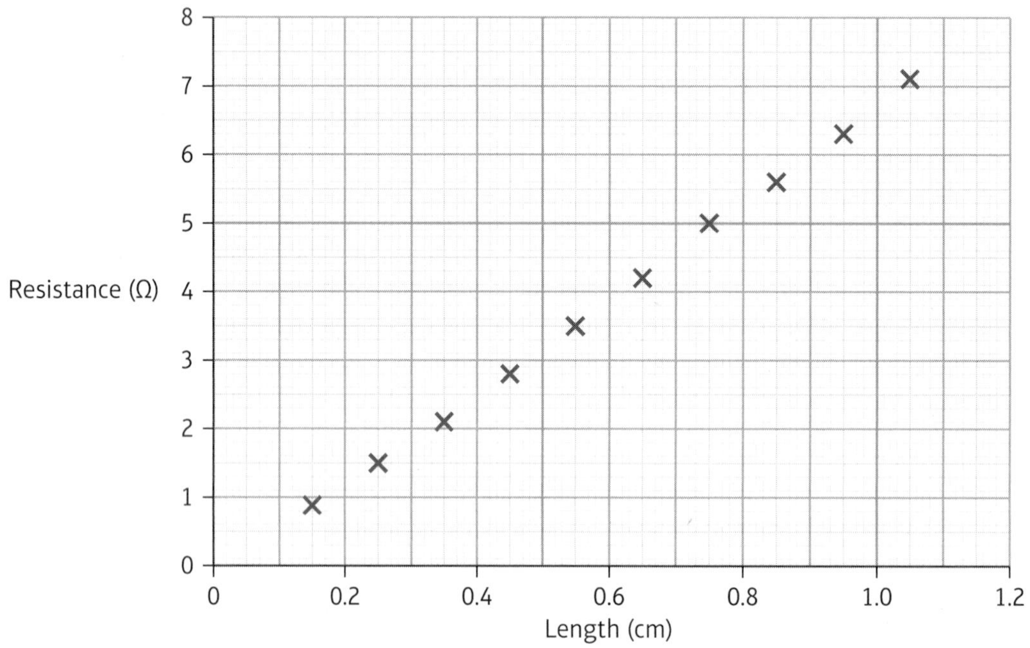

01.5 Draw the line of best fit. **[1 mar**

01.6 What conclusion can you draw from this graph? **[1 mar**

01.7 Use your graph to find the resistance of a piece of wire of length 1 m. **[1 mar**

Diodes, filament bulbs and resistors all respond differently when potential differences are applied to them. A diode has a low resistance if the potential difference (p.d.) is in one direction but a very high resistance if the potential difference is in the opposite direction. This means that current can only flow in one direction. You will investigate these three devices and produce a graph of current (A) against potential difference (V) for each one.

Your teacher may watch to see if you can:

- follow instructions carefully
- work safely.

Core learning outcomes: I am able to…
use appropriate apparatus to measure current and potential difference and to explore the characteristics of a variety of circuit elements
use circuit diagrams to construct and check series and parallel circuits, including a variety of common circuit elements.

Practical Objective

To investigate what happens to the current through three different components (resistor, diode and filament lamp) when the p.d. across them changes.

Content Objective

A resistor at constant temperature has a constant resistance so that current is proportional to potential difference. Resistance of a filament lamp and a diode changes depending on the current passing through the component.

Hypothesis

Write down hypotheses for the resistor, filament lamp and diode for this experiment. You may wish to include sketch graphs.

Task 1: To investigate *I–V* characteristics for a resistor

Method

A Use a low voltage power supply that allows you to vary the potential difference, or a variable resistor. Your teacher will explain this to you.

B Set up the circuit as shown in the diagram below. Ensure that, when the circuit is switched on, both the ammeter and voltmeter have *positive* readings. If either meter has a negative value, swap over the connecting leads on the terminals going into the meter.

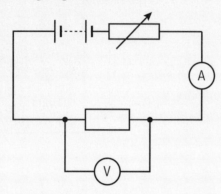

C Record the current using the ammeter and the potential difference using the voltmeter in the table on the next page.

D Adjust the variable resistor or low voltage supply and record the new current and potential difference readings.

E Repeat step **D**.

F Switch off the circuit and reverse the connections going into the power supply.

G Ensure that when you switch on the circuit this time, there are negative readings on both meters.

H Repeat steps **C**–**E**.

I Plot a graph of current against voltage on the graph paper on page 80.

Task 2: To investigate *I–V* characteristics for a filament lamp

Method

Use the Method from **Task 1** to repeat your experiment using a filament lamp. Set up the circuit as shown in the diagram below. Record your readings in the table on the next page and plot your graph using the graph paper on page 80.

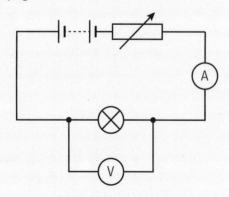

Apparatus

- connecting leads
- low voltage power supply
- resistor
- ammeter
- voltmeter
- variable resistor

Safety

- Ask your teacher to check you circuit before you switch it or

Apparatus

- connecting leads
- low voltage power supply
- filament lamp
- ammeter
- voltmeter
- variable resistor

Safety

- Ask your teacher to check you circuit before you switch it on. Take care with the lamp: i could get hot enough to burn your skin.

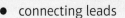
Task 3: To investigate *I–V* characteristics for a diode

Method

Use a low voltage power supply that allows you to vary the potential difference, or a variable resistor. Your teacher will explain this to you.

Set up the circuit as shown in the diagram below. It looks similar to the previous experiments but has a couple of changes. The diode must be protected with a protective resistor to stop the current through it becoming too large. The ammeter will need to be replaced with a milliammeter due to the low currents flowing through it. Do not alter the potential difference to make it greater than 6 V.

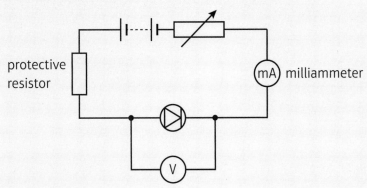

protective resistor

mA milliammeter

V

Ensure that, when the circuit is switched on, both the ammeter and voltmeter have *positive* readings. If either meter has a negative value, swap over the connecting leads on the terminals going into the meter.

- Record the new current and potential difference values in the table below.

Adjust the variable resistor or low voltage supply and record new current and potential difference readings.

Repeat step **E**.

- Switch off the circuit and swap over the connections going into the power supply.

- Ensure that when you switch on the circuit this time, there are negative readings on both meters.

Repeat steps **D–F**.

Plot a graph of current against voltage on the graph paper on the next page.

Considering your results/conclusions

Use the space below to record the results from all three of your experiments. You should have four or five readings for each Task.

Task 1 (resistor)		Task 2 (filament lamp)		Task 3 (diode)	
Current (A)	Voltage (V)	Current (A)	Voltage (V)	Current (A)	Voltage (V)

2 Draw a graph for the resistor in blue, the filament lamp in red and the diode in black. Current (the dependent variable) should go on the *y*-axis and potential difference (the independent variable) should go on the *x*-axis. You will have negative values so the origin (at 0 V, 0 A) will be in the middle of the graph paper. If you are unsure, ask your teacher about the likely shape for the graph. Draw a line of best fit through your points for each graph. Each graph should pass through the origin (i.e. at 0 V the current should be 0 A).

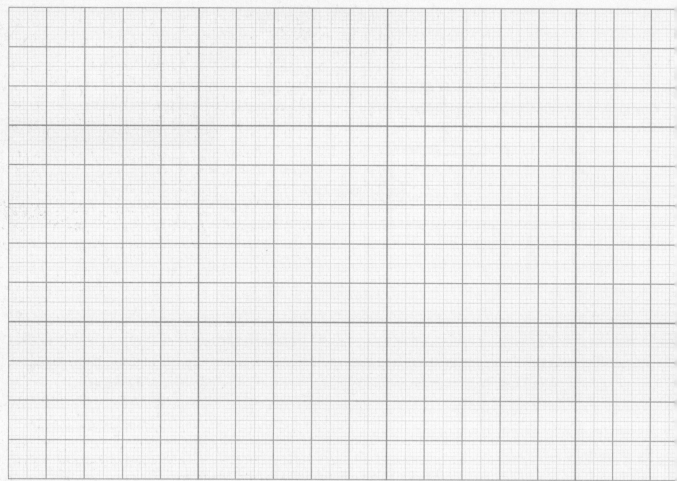

3 Use your results from all three experiments to describe the relationship between potential difference, current a resistance for:

a a resistor

b a filament lamp

c   a diode.

Evaluation

Describe how you tried to ensure the measurements you recorded were as accurate as possible.

Describe what you could do to make your investigation more accurate.

Look at a textbook or website and find some published current–potential difference (I–V) graphs for a resistor, a filament lamp and a diode. Do the shape of your graphs match the examples you found? Explain your answer. Was your hypothesis correct?

Exam-style questions

01   A student measured the potential difference and current of a resistor and recorded the values in the table below.

Current (A)	Voltage (V)	Resistance (Ω)
0.052	0.5	
0.100	1.0	
0.153	1.5	
0.197	2.0	
0.252	2.5	
0.298	3.0	

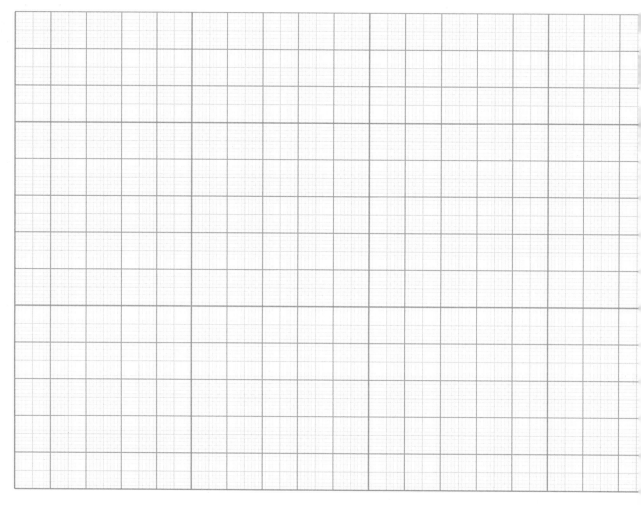

01.1   On the axes provided, draw a graph of potential difference on the *y*-axis and current on the *x*-axis using the values recorded by the student.

Label the axes, including the units, and make sure you use a suitable scale.   **[2 mark**

01.2   Plot the points and draw a line of best fit.   **[3 mark**

01.3   Complete the table by finding the value of the resistance for each set of values. Calculate the mean value of the resistance.   **[3 mark**

1.4 Use the graph to find the resistance of the resistor. **[3 marks]**

1.5 Compare your results from questions **01.3** and **01.4** and explain why a graph produces a more accurate result. **[2 marks]**

1.6 Draw a second graph to represent a resistor with a lower resistance and label it B. **[1 mark]**

1.7 Give and explain the relationship between current and voltage as shown by the graph. **[2 marks]**

1.8 Name the law which this represents. **[1 mark]**

1.9 What name is given to conductors that obey this law? **[1 mark]**

The density of a substance is the mass of a unit volume of that substance. Almost all substances are most dense when they are solids and least dense when they are gases. The arrangement of particles can explain the differences in density between different states of matter. A solid substance is usually more dense than the same substance as a liquid, because the particles in solids are closer together. The exception to this is water, where the liquid is more dense than the solid (ice).

You will complete three experiments on density. You will determine the density of liquids and solid objects with both regular and irregular shapes.

Your teacher may watch to see if you can:

- follow instructions carefully
- take careful measurements
- work safely.

Core learning outcomes: I am able to…
use appropriate apparatus to make and record accurate measurements of length, area, mass and volume
use such measurements to determine the density of solid objects and liquids.

Practical Objective

To identify a substance from its density.

Content Objective

Density is mass per unit volume.

Apparatus

- balance
- solid objects/blocks with regular shapes
- 30 cm ruler

Task 1: To determine the density of regular shaped objects

Method

A Select four different regular shaped objects from the selection provided. If they have labels, write these in the first column of the table on the next page. Otherwise, write a brief description (e.g. black cube).

B Measure all the dimensions (length, width and height) for each object to one decimal place using a 30 cm ruler. Record your results in centimetres in the table on the next page.

C Measure the mass of each object in grams using a balance and record this in the table on the next page.

Combined science

Recording your results

To calculate volume (column **6**), multiply length (column **2**) by width (column **3**) by height (column **4**).
Volume = length × width × height

To calculate density (column **7**), use the equation:

$$\text{density (g/cm}^3\text{)} = \frac{\text{mass (g)}}{\text{volume (cm}^3\text{)}}$$

1	2	3	4	5	6	7	8
Object	Length in cm	Width in cm	Height in cm	Mass in g	Volume in cm³	Density in g/cm³	Material substance is made from

Use the table below to work out what each substance is and complete column **8**.

Substance	Aluminium	Brass	Copper	Iron	Lead	Wood	Zinc
Density in g/cm³	2.70	8.55	8.92	7.80	11.34	0.71	7.14

Compare your answers to the correct answers for each material given in the table above. How well did you do?

_____
_____
_____
_____
_____
_____
_____
_____
_____
_____
_____

Task 2: To determine the density of irregular shaped objects

Method

A Choose an object with an irregular shape from the selection provided and measure its mass using the balance. Write the name of the material and the mass of the object in the table below. Tie some thread or very thin string around the object.

B Stand a displacement can on the bench with its spout over a bowl. Fill the can with water until the water just starts to come out of the spout.

C When it has stopped dripping, hold a measuring cylinder under the spout and carefully lower the object into the can using the string.

D Stand the measuring cylinder on the bench and read the volume of water you have collected. This is the same as the volume of your object. Record this volume in the table below.

E Repeat steps **A–D** with four more objects with irregular shapes.

Practical Objective

To find the density of solid objects with irregular shapes.

Content Objective

To calculate the density of solid objects with irregular shapes, the volume of the objects can be measured through displacement of a liquid medium.

Apparatus

- balance
- displacement can
- measuring cylinder
- bowl
- solid objects with irregular shapes
- thread or very thin string

Safety

- Mop up any spills straight away.

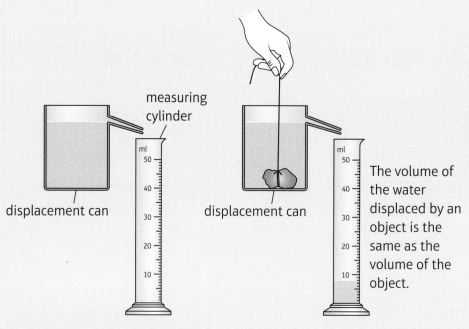

The volume of the water displaced by an object is the same as the volume of the object.

Recording your results

1 Complete the table below.

Material	Mass in g	Volume in cm³	Density in g/cm³

2 Calculate the density of each object and write it in the table. The equation you need is:

$$\text{density (g/cm}^3) = \frac{\text{mass (g)}}{\text{volume (cm}^3)}$$

Task 3: Densities of liquids

Method

Zero the balance. Place an empty measuring cylinder on the balance and record its mass.

Carefully pour 50 cm³ of a liquid into the measuring cylinder. Write down the name of the liquid and the reading on the balance. Subtract the mass of the empty measuring cylinder from this reading to calculate the mass of 50 cm³ of the liquid.

Repeat step **B** with four more liquids, washing your measuring cylinder each time before replacing the liquid.

Recording your results

Complete the table below.

Liquid	Mass of 50 cm³ (g)	Density (g/cm³)

Calculate the density of each liquid and write it in the table. The equation you need is:

$$\text{density (g/cm}^3) = \frac{\text{mass (g)}}{\text{volume (cm}^3)}$$

Considering your results/conclusions

a What was the range of densities for the solids you measured?

_____

_____

_____

b What was the range of densities for the liquids?

_____

_____

_____

Compare the densities of the solids and liquids that you tested.

_____

_____

_____

_____

_____

Practical Objective

To find the density of a liquid

Content Objective

Different concentrations of the same solute in solution will have differing densities.

Apparatus

- balance
- measuring cylinder
- beaker
- liquids, such as water and sugar or salt solutions of various concentrations

Safety ⚠

- Mop up any spills straight away.

Exam-style questions

01 A student wants to calculate the density of the two objects shown.

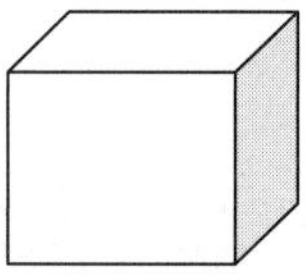

cube of metal    **pound coin**

01.1 Describe the measurements that the student should take and how the student would use these measurements to calculate the densities of the two objects. You may wish to draw a small diagram above to help your explanation of the pound coin.

a Cube of metal [4 mar

b Pound coin [4 mar

01.2 **a** Calculate the mass of a cube of length 3 cm if its density is 0.6 g/cm³. Include an appropriate unit of mass. [3 mar

b Explain whether the cube will float or sink in water. [2 mar

c Calculate the density of the pound coin if its mass is 9.5 g and volume is 1.25 cm³. Include an appropriate unit of density. [2 mar

esigners need to know the characteristics of springs so that they can choose
he best spring for their purpose. The extension of a spring (or other object)
 the change in length when forces are applied. You will investigate this
elationship by applying weights to a spring and measuring the extension.
ou will use the information to calculate work done to stretch the spring.

our teacher may watch to see if you can:

 take careful measurements.

Core learning outcomes: I am able to…
use appropriate apparatus to make and record length accurately
use appropriate apparatus to measure and observe the effect of force on the extension of springs and collect the data required to plot a force-extension graph.

ethod

Set up the apparatus as shown in the diagram, making sure the metre ruler is vertical.

Measure the length of the spring with no masses, just the mass hanger hanging on it and write it down.

Hang a 50 g mass on the mass hanger. Record the extension of the spring (the new length – original length of the spring).

Repeat step **C** until you have found the extension of the spring with 10 different masses. Each 50 g mass puts a downwards force of 0.5 N on the spring.

If you have time, repeat steps **A** to **D** for a different spring.

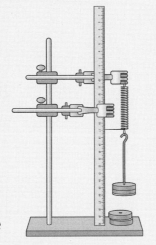

Practical Objective

To investigate the extension and work done when applying forces to a spring.

Content Objective

Provided the spring has not been inelastically deformed, the force applied is proportional to the extension and the work done on the spring is equal to the elastic potential energy stored in the spring.

Apparatus

- eye protection
- stand and two clamps; and G clamp or heavy weight to prevent stand from toppling
- springs, with pointers attached at the bottom
- metre ruler
- masses

Safety ⚠

- Wear eye protection.

Recording your results

Record your results in the table below. Calculate the average extension for each spring and record it in the table.

| Force (N) | Spring 1 | | Spring 2 | |
	Extension (cm)	Extension (m)	Extension (cm)	Extension (m)
0	0	0		
0.5				
Average				

2 Plot a graph of force (in N) on the vertical axis and average extension (in m) on the horizontal axis, and draw a line of best fit.
If you repeated the experiment with a second spring, plot a graph of these results on the same diagram.

90

Considering your results/conclusions

3 Are your data of good quality? Explain your answer.

4 Calculate the gradient of the line on your graph(s). The gradient gives you the spring constant for each spring.

The spring constant gives a measure of how stiff a spring is. How can you work out which springs should feel the stiffest by looking at their spring constants?

Explain how you would find the mass of an unknown object using the graph you have plotted.

The work done to stretch a spring can be calculated using the following equation:

energy transferred in stretching (J) $= \frac{1}{2} \times$ spring constant (N/m) $\times$ extension^2 (m)^2

Calculate the energy transferred in stretching each spring that you tested.

Exam-style questions

01 A student suspended a spring from a laboratory stand. The student then attached a mass to the base of the spring to investigate how the spring's extension related to the weight of the mass.

The student used a ruler to measure the extension of the spring. However, the ruler was not vertical when t student measured the extension.

01.1 How would this affect the extension data recorded? **[1 ma**

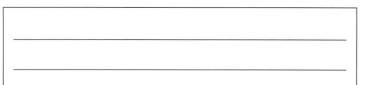

01.2 What type of error is this? **[1 ma**

The student adjusted the ruler to make it vertical. They then obtained the data shown in the graph below.

01.3 Describe the relationship between weight and extension shown in the graph. **[2 marks]**

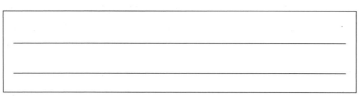

01.4 Name the law that this shows and write it as an equation. **[3 marks]**

01.5 What is the value of the limit of proportionality of the spring? **[1 mark]**

01.6 Calculate the spring constant for the spring. Include an appropriate unit. **[3 mark**

01.7 Draw a line on the graph to represent the behaviour of a spring with a higher spring constant. **[1 mar**

Combined science

In this practical you will apply different forces to a trolley or a toy car. You will also vary the mass of the car or trolley, but keep the force constant. In each case you will time how long it takes for the car or trolley to move a certain distance and calculate the acceleration of the toy car or trolley.

Part 1: Measuring the effect of force on acceleration at constant mass

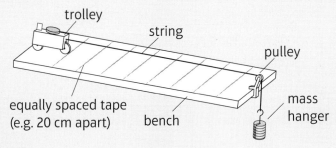

trolley
string
pulley
equally spaced tape
(e.g. 20 cm apart)
bench
mass hanger

Hypothesis

Write down your hypothesis.

Method

A. Use the ruler to mark lines at 20 cm intervals on the bench. Draw straight lines at these intervals or place tape across the bench. Use the diagram to guide you.

B. Attach the bench pulley to one end of the bench.

C. Tie a length of string to the trolley or toy car and pass the string over the pulley. Tie the mass hanger to the other end of the string.

D. Place the trolley or toy car at the start point and make sure the string is horizontal and in line with it.

E. You will need to try using different masses on the mass hanger to find a suitable range to use for your car/trolley. The range is suitable when the car accelerates gradually, allowing you to measure the time it passes each interval. Hold the trolley or toy car firmly when you attach the masses.

F. With just the mass hanger attached, release the trolley or toy car and simultaneously start the stopwatch. Press the stopwatch (in lap mode) as the trolley or toy car passes each measured interval on the bench and for the final time at 100 cm. You could also use a smartphone to video the sequence, which provides more reliable data.

G. Record the results in the table, remembering to convert mass to force by multiplying the mass (in kg) by 10.

H. Repeat steps **E** to **G** for increasing masses.

Practical Objective

Part 1: To investigate the effect of mass on the acceleration of a trolley.

Part 2: To investigate the effect of force on the acceleration of a trolley.

Content Objective

Newton's second law: the acceleration of an object is proportional to the force applied and inversely proportional to the mass of the object or $F = m \times a$

Apparatus

- a trolley or toy car
- a metre ruler
- pencil or masking tape
- a bench pulley
- string
- a mass hanger and 50 g and 100 g masses
- crumpled paper
- a stopwatch
- sticky tack

Safety

- Place crumpled paper on floor below masses to catch them in case they fall.

Results

Force (N)	Time taken to travel a certain distance (s)				
	20 cm	40 cm	60 cm	80 cm	100 cm

1 Calculate the acceleration of the trolley/car at 20 cm, 40 cm, 60 cm, 80 cm and 100 cm intervals using $s = ut + \frac{1}{2}a$
   Record your results in the space below and calculate a mean for each force.

Force (N)	Acceleration at each distance interval (m/s²)					Mean
	20 cm	40 cm	60 cm	80 cm	100 cm	

Now plot a graph of force (*y*-axis) against mean acceleration (*x*-axis) and draw a line of best fit.

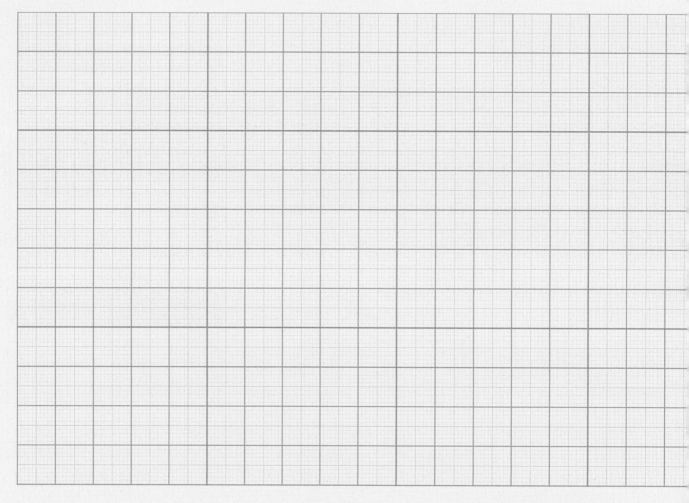

2 What is the relationship between the force applied to the car and the acceleration of the car?

3 Was your prediction correct?

Part 2: Measuring the effect of mass on acceleration with a constant force

Hypothesis

Write down your hypothesis.

_____

_____

_____

Apparatus

- eye protection
- stand and two clamps
- springs
- ruler
- masses

Safety

- Place crumpled paper on floor below masses to catch them in case they fall.

Method

A Set up the bench, bench pulley, mass hanger and trolley or toy car as in steps **A** to **D** of Part 1.

B Use your results from Part 1 to select a mass for the mass hanger that will just accelerate the trolley or toy car along the bench. Record the mass of the trolley or toy car.

C Attach your chosen mass to the end of the string. This will provide a constant force on the trolley or toy car. Hold the trolley or toy car firmly when you attach the masses.

D Release the trolley or toy car and simultaneously start the stopwatch. Press the stopwatch (in lap mode) as the trolley or toy car passes each measured interval on the bench and for the final time at 100 cm. You could also use a smart phone to video the sequence, which provides more reliable data.

E Record your results in the table below.

F Repeat steps **C** to **E** for **four** more readings, increasing the mass of the car each time.

Results

Mass of car (kg)	Time taken to travel each distance (s)				
	20 cm	40 cm	60 cm	80 cm	100 cm

Calculate the acceleration of the trolley/car at 20 cm, 40 cm, 60 cm, 80 cm and 100 cm intervals using $s = ut + \frac{1}{2}at^2$.

Record your results in the space below and calculate a mean for each mass.

Mass of car (kg)	Acceleration at each distance interval (m/s²)					
	20 cm	40 cm	60 cm	80 cm	100 cm	Mean

Now plot a graph of mass (*y*-axis) against acceleration (*x*-axis) and draw a line of best fit.

2 What is the relationship between the mass of the car and the acceleration of the car?

3 Was your prediction correct?

4 Do the results of the two activities support Newton's second law?

5 Identify the sources of error in these two investigations. Are they random or systematic?

6 How could you improve the accuracy of your results?

xam-style questions

1   A student used light gates and a datalogger to investigate the effect that varying the force (caused by the masses on the mass hanger) would have on the acceleration of the trolley along the ramp.

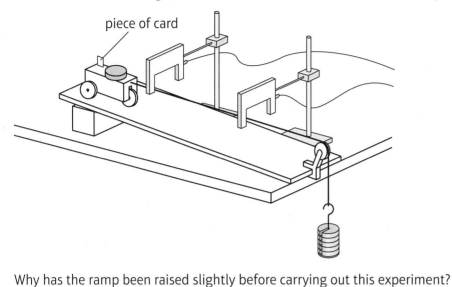

piece of card

1.1   Why has the ramp been raised slightly before carrying out this experiment?   **[1 mark]**

1.2   What must the student keep constant during this experiment?   **[1 mark]**

1.3   Draw a results table in the space below for the student to record their measurements for five different forces. Include a column to show how they would calculate the acceleration of the trolley from these measurements.   **[5 marks]**

01.4 The student plots a graph of force against acceleration.

Sketch it on the axes provided and describe the relationship shown. **[3 mar**

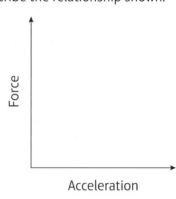

_____

_____

01.5 Write down an expression for Newton's second law. **[2 mar**

_____

_____

01.6 The force applied to a toy car of mass 450 g is 2.0 N. Calculate its acceleration and include an appropriate unit. **[3 mar**

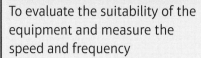

Light waves do not travel very far through sea water before being absorbed by the water or reflected by tiny particles in the water. This makes it impossible to take pictures of things that are deep down on the sea bed. Scientists and explorers use sonar equipment to send sound waves into the water and detect echoes. The depth can be worked out from the speed of sound in the water and the time it takes for the echo to return. The speed, frequency and wavelength of waves can be measured in different ways. The most suitable equipment for making these measurements depends on the type of wave and on its speed. You are going to use different pieces of equipment to measure the speed and wavelength of waves on the surface of water, and the speed and frequency of sound waves in solids.

Your teacher may watch to see if you can:

- follow instructions carefully
- make accurate measurements.

Core learning outcomes: I am able to…

make observations of waves in fluids and solids to identify the suitability of apparatus to measure speed, frequency and wavelength.

Part 1: Speed of waves on water

Method

A. Set up a ripple tank with a straight dipper close to one of the short sides of the tank and a piece of white card on the floor below. Place a ruler next to the card.

B. Count how many waves are formed in 10 seconds and record this number in the space below.

C. Look at the waves against the ruler. Use the markings on the ruler to estimate the wavelength of the waves. If you have a camera, use it to take a photo of the waves with the ruler next to the card on the floor. Record your estimated wavelength below.

D. Mark two points on the edge of the card and measure the distance between them. Use the stopwatch to find out how long it takes a wave to travel from one mark to the other. Record this value below.

Practical Objective

To evaluate the suitability of the equipment and measure the speed and frequency

Part 1: of waves on the surface of water

Part 2: of sound waves in solids.

Content Objective

Wave speed = frequency × wavelength

Apparatus

- ripple tank
- stop clock
- ruler
- digital camera

Safety

- Mop up any spilled water straight away. Refer to section 12 of CLEAPSS G77 on the safe use of ripple tanks for those with photosensitivity.

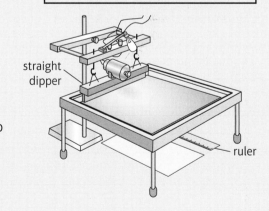

straight dipper

ruler

Recording your results

Number of waves counted [step **B**]	
Estimated wavelength [step **C**]	
Distance between two points [step **D**]	
Time taken for wave to travel between two points [step **D**]	

Using your results

1 Calculate the speed of a single wave by dividing the distance by the time (both from step **D**). Make sure your distance is in metres and your time is in seconds.

2 Find the frequency by taking the number of waves in 10 seconds (from step **B**) and dividing by 10. Then calculate the speed of the series of waves by multiplying the wavelength (from step **C**) by the frequency you have just worked out.

Considering your results/conclusions

3 Compare your results from questions **1** and **2** above with the results obtained by other groups. Are your results similar? If not, can you explain the differences?

Evaluation

4 How easy was it to measure the frequency in step **B**? Why did you count the number of waves in 10 seconds?

5 How easy was it to measure the wavelength in step **C**? It was suggested that you use a camera to help you do this. What is the benefit of doing this?

6 How easy was it to time a single wave in step **D**? Is there any way you could improve this measurement?

Part 2: Measuring waves in a solid

Method

Suspend a metal rod horizontally using clamp stands and rubber bands, as shown in the diagram below.

Hit one end of the rod with a hammer. Hold a smartphone with a frequency app close to the rod and note down the peak frequency.

Measure the length of the rod and write it down. The wavelength will be twice the length of the rod. Record the wavelength in the space below. Repeat steps **A** to **C** using the second metal rod.

Practical Objective

To measure the speed and frequency of sound waves in solids and evaluate the suitability of the equipment.

Content Objective

Sound waves can travel through solids, causing vibrations.

Apparatus

- metre rule
- hammer
- two clamps and stands
- two long metal rods of different lengths but the same material
- rubber bands
- smartphone with frequency app

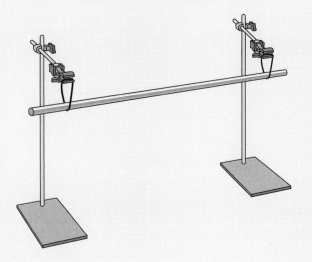

Recording your results

	Metal rod 1	Metal rod 2
Frequency [step **B**]		
Wavelength [step **C**]		

Use the frequency (from step **B**) and the wavelength (from step **C**) to calculate the speed of sound in the metal rods.

Considering your results/conclusions

What is the speed of sound in the material you tested?

_____

_____

Evaluation

3 Explain which of your measurements is more accurate: the wavelength or the frequency.

4 Complete the table below to summarise the equipment you used for the measurements in both parts of this investigation. Assess how suitable the equipment was.

What was measured?	Which material was this measured for?	How was it measured?	Why was this method chosen?

5 You can measure walking speed using a tape measure and a stop clock. Explain why these instruments are not suitable for measuring the speed of sound in a solid.

Exam-style questions

01 Small water waves are created in a ripple tank by a wooden bar. The wooden bar vibrates, hitting the surface of the water.

The diagram below shows a cross-section of the ripple tank and water.

01.1 Which arrow, **A**, **B** or **C**, shows the amplitude of a water wave? **[1 mar**

01.2 Explain what we would hear when a sound wave has a high amplitude. **[1 mark]**

01.3 The wooden bar is moved up and down faster so that it hits the water more often.

Explain how this affects the wave frequency? **[1 mark]**

01.4 Describe the sound heard if a note of a higher frequency is played on a flute. **[1 mark]**

01.5 Describe how you would measure the wavelength of the water waves in a ripple tank.

Explain the steps you would take to ensure accurate measurements. **[2 marks]**

01.6 If the distance **AC** = 5 cm, calculate the wavelength of the wave in the ripple tank. **[1 mark]**

01.7 Give the equation relating wave speed, frequency and wavelength. **[2 marks]**

01.8 The water waves in a ripple tank have a frequency of 20 Hz. Calculate the speed of the waves using the value of wavelength you calculated in question **01.6**. **[2 marks]**

A radiator in a car is designed to transfer energy to the outside air, to stop the engine overheating. Radiators for cooling car engines were patented over 100 years ago, in 1879. Radiators are often painted to assist energy transfer by radiation. Surfaces affect how much energy is transferred by radiation from different objects. You will investigate the effect of different coloured surfaces on the amount of energy transferred by radiation from a tube of hot water.

Your teacher may watch to see if you can:

- take careful measurements
- present your results as a line graph.

Core learning outcomes: I am able to…
use appropriate apparatus to make and record temperature accurately
make observations of the effects of the interaction of electromagnetic waves with matter.

Method

A Cover each of the four boiling tubes in a different coloured paper. Use the same thickness for each tube. Fasten the paper in place with sticky tape.

B Use the measuring cylinder to pour the same volume of hot water from a kettle into each tube.

C Measure the temperature of the water in each tube and start the stop clock.

D Record the temperature of the water in each tube every two minutes for 20 minutes.

Recording your results

1 Record your results in the table below.

Practical Objective

To investigate the effect of different coloured surfaces on the amount of energy transferred by radiation.

Content Objective

Dark surfaces are good absorbers and emitters of radiation, light surfaces are good reflectors of radiation.

Apparatus

- four boiling tubes
- test tube rack
- measuring cylinder
- four thermometers
- stop clock
- four different coloured papers, preferably matt black, shiny black, matt white and shiny white
- sticky tape
- hot water

Safety

- Take care with hot water.

Time (min)	Temperature (°C)			
	Tube 1	Tube 2	Tube 3	Tube 4
0				
2				
4				
6				
8				
10				
12				
14				
16				
18				
20				

Draw a line graph to present your results. Time (the independent variable) should go on the x-axis and temperature (the dependent variable) should go on the y-axis. Plot all four sets of results on the same axes and join each set of points with a smooth curve of best fit.

Considering your results/conclusions

Describe what your graph shows about the rate of cooling of the water in each tube.

_____

_____

_____

_____

Which colour is best at emitting radiation? Which is the worst? Explain your conclusion.

_____

_____

_____

_____

_____

Evaluation

5 How well do your results support your conclusion? Your answer should refer to your graph.

6 Can you draw a general conclusion from your results (such as, light colours emit more radiation than dark colours)? Explain your answer.

Exam-style questions

01 **Student A** decides to investigate the amount of infrared radiation emitted by different coloured surfaces using a Leslie cube.

This is the method used.

1. To make the Leslie cube, the student paints the four sides of a hollow copper cube matt black, shiny black, silver and matt white.

2. The student fills the cube with hot water and uses an infrared detector to measure the radiation emitte from each surface.

01.1 Name the variables which must be controlled. **[2 mar**

1.2 Name the independent and the dependent variables. **[2 marks]**

Independent

_____

Dependent

_____

1.3 Explain why **Student A** places the infrared detector at the same distance from the surface of the Leslie cube each time a measurement is taken. **[1 mark]**

_____

_____

1.4 Another student, **Student B**, uses a thermometer to take temperature measurements close to each surface of the cube. The thermometer touches the shiny silver side of the cube during measurement.

Explain why this makes the second student's measurement less valid and suggest how the student can improve on this method. **[2 marks]**

_____

_____

_____

1.5 The students compared their results. Identify **two** possible differences between their results and give reasons.

Difference 1 **[4 marks]**

_____

_____

Reason

_____

_____

Difference 2

_____

_____

Reason

_____

_____

Word	Meaning
accuracy	How close a value is to its real value.
anomalous	Does not fit a pattern.
caution	Means 'beware'.
chemical reaction	A change in which one or more new substances are formed.
chromatogram	The results of chromatography (e.g. a dried piece of paper for paper chromatography), when the dissolved solids have been separated.
circuit diagram	A diagram drawn with standard symbols and straight lines to represent an electrical circuit.
column graph	Another term for 'bar chart'.
control variables	Variables whose values need to be kept steady during an investigation.
correlation	A relationship between two variables. If an increase in one is linked to an increase in the other, it is 'positive'. An increase in one linked to a decrease in the other is 'negative'.
data	Observations or measurements collected in investigations.
decimal places	The number of digits after the decimal point.
dependent variable	The variable that is measured in an investigation. The values of the dependent variable depend on those of the independent variable.
directly proportional relationship	A relationship between two variables where one variable doubles when the other doubles. The graph is a straight line through (0,0). We say that one variable is directly proportional to the other.
discrete data	Data given in the form of limited values. For example, shoe sizes come in whole sizes and half sizes but not in sizes in between. So size 4, size 4½ and size 5 are all possible, but size 4.149 is not. The number of different shoe sizes is limited. ab Bool
estimate	An approximate answer, often calculated from a sample or using rounded values.
evidence	Data used to support an idea or show that it is wrong.
extension	The length by which a material extends or is compressed when a certain force is applied. It is the length of the material after the application of the force minus the original length.
hazard	Something that could cause harm.
hazard symbol	A warning symbol that shows why something can cause harm.
hypothesis	An idea about how something works that can be tested using experiments. The plural is *hypotheses*.
independent variable	The variable that you chose the values of in an investigation.
interval	The gap between one value of an independent variable and the next, in an investigation.
linear relationship	A relationship between variables that produces a straight line when plotted on a scatter graph. The line does *not* have to go through the (0,0) point.
line graph	A graph used to show how a variable changes with time.
line of best fit	A line going through a set of points on a graph, so that roughly equal numbers of points end up on either side of the line.
mean	An average calculated by adding up the values of a set of measurements and dividing by the number of measurements in the set.
median	The middle value in a set of values that has been written in order.
mode	The most common value in a set of values.
model	A way of showing or representing a phenomenon that helps you to think about it or to investigate it.

outlier	Another term for 'anomalous reading'.
peer review	An evaluation of the quality of a scientific paper carried out by other scientists conduct research in the same area of science.
precision	How close a set of repeated measurements are to one another.
prediction	What you think will happen in an experiment.
qualitative data	Data that is not in form of numbers (e.g. the names of colours).
random error	A mistake made in a measurement, which can be different every time that measurement is made.
range	The highest and lowest values in a set of data.
relationship	A link between two variables.
repeatable	Results that are similar when repeated by the same experimenter. You can be more certain that a set of repeatable results is correct.
reproducible	Results that are similar when repeated by different experimenters.
risk	The chance of harm being caused by a hazard.
sample	To take a small part of something to investigate. You use a sample to draw conclusions about the larger whole.
scatter graph	A graph in which data for two variables are plotted as points. This allows you to see whether there is a relationship between the two variables.
significant figures	The number of digits of a value, starting from the first non-zero digit.
systematic error	An error that is the same for all readings, such as forgetting to zero a balance before using it to measure a series of masses.
theory	A hypothesis (or set of hypotheses) that has been repeatedly confirmed through experiment and for which there is a high degree of agreement in the scientific community.
trial run	A quick, rough version of an experiment that is carried out to ensure that the main experiment is designed well.
variable	Anything that can change and be measured.

Microscopy

drawings for Methods 1, 2 and 3. Cells should be drawn with a sharp pencil and clean lines. Labelling lines should be drawn with a ruler and should not overlap. Your writing should be neat. The magnification or scale should be added to show the size of the cells.

Osmosis

Your own prediction.

–5 Your own results.

Mean calculated from your results.

Your own graph.

The potato slices that gained mass did so because water moved by osmosis into the root from the surrounding solution. The potato slices that lost mass did so because water moved by osmosis from the root into the surrounding solution. Any potato slices that didn't change mass would have been in a solution with the same solute concentration as the potato cells.

Percentage change removes any variation due to differences in initial mass between slices.

0 Calculating a mean takes away or reduces the impact of any possible anomalous results which could be caused by variations between the potatoes.

1 Your own suggestion.

2 Divide the change in mass by the length of time the potatoes were left in the sucrose solution.

3 Food tests

1 Your results will depend on the foods supplied and tested. The table shows some typical results.

Food	Iodine test	Benedict's test	Biuret test	Emulsion test
full-fat milk	yellow–orange	yellow	purple	cloudy
whey	yellow–orange	bright blue	purple	clear
egg white	yellow–orange	bright blue	purple	clear
potato	black–blue	bright blue	light blue	clear
glucose	yellow–orange	red precipitate	light blue	clear
(icing sugar)	yellow–orange	bright blue	light blue	clear

2 Your answers will depend on the foods supplied and tested.

3 Both the test for reducing sugars and the test for proteins could give an indication of the quantity of substance present, based on the colour produced.
In the test for reducing sugar, the colour changes from light blue (no reducing sugar) to green/blue, then orange and eventually red (lots of reducing sugar). This gives an indication of the amount of reducing sugar present.
In the protein test, the purple colour produced will be more darker the more protein is present.

4 This will depend on the results obtained if they were not as expected. Errors are most likely to occur if equipment is not cleaned properly between tests and food becomes contaminated with another sample. Therefore, it would be a good idea to ensure equipment (e.g. glassware, spatulas etc.) is cleaned between tests. Using coloured foods may make some colour changes more difficult to see. To overcome this problem, select foods that have neutral or muted colours.

4 Enzymes

1 Your own prediction and explanation.

2–3 Your own results. Make sure each of the column headings in your table is clear.

4 Your own graph.

5–6 Your own description and suggestion.

7 Qualitative: the test only tells you if there is starch present or not. It cannot show how much is present/left.

8–11 Your own answers.

5 Photosynthesis

1–2 Your own results.

3 Your own graph.

4 Your own description and explanation.

5 H Light intensity varies with distance according to the inverse square law. So, if you double the distance from the light source (move the lamp away), the light intensity is $\frac{1}{2^2}$ or $\frac{1}{4}$ times the original intensity (it reduces to a quarter of the original value). If you halve the distance to the light source (move the lamp closer), light intensity is $\frac{1}{\left(\frac{1}{2}\right)^2}$ which is 4 times the original.

This is the pattern you should see in the graph. Take a measurement in the middle of your values and look at what happens when that result is doubled or halved to see if it fits the inverse square law. Plotting the rate of photosynthesis against the inverse squared distance from the source ($1/\text{distance}^2$) should give you a straight-line graph.

6 To show that light is required for the algal balls to photosynthesise. No colour change should have occurred in the control bottle, proving that light is required by the algal balls.

6 Reaction time

1 This is likely to be a bar chart. The dependent variable (the results) should be on the y-axis and the independent variable (the students taking part in the experiment) should be on the x-axis.

2 a Your own answer.

b There could be a correlation between fast reaction times and skill at reaction sports (basketball, football, hockey or tennis for example). The same is somewhat true for video games but this does depend on the style of game being played.

3 Your results are likely to improve as you practise more and learn what to expect. But they will also plateau. You can only get so quick on this test without resorting to cheating (e.g. anticipating and closing your hand before the ruler is dropped).

4 Some possible ways to improve the experiment include: increasing the number of repeats to ten drops per person, changing the hand to see if there is a difference with the other hand, altering the dropping point of the ruler.

5 Use a computer program or app where you have to press a button when a light or image is displayed. This would collect all of the data and ensure that reaction times are correctly measured.

7 Field investigations

1–7 Your own results/answers.

8 Making salts

1 The crystals are blue and diamond shaped. (The size will vary depending on conditions.)

2 a clear solution
b black solid (powder)
c blue solution

3 copper oxide + sulfuric acid → copper sulfate + water

4 So that all the acid is used up.

5 copper oxide

6 copper sulfate

7 This is known as a neutralisation reaction because the hydrog ions of the acid are removed (and a salt and water are formed The hydrogen ions make the initial solution acidic, but the fin solution is neutral (because both the salt and water are neut substances).

8 copper oxide

9 $CuO(s) + H_2SO_4(aq) \rightarrow CuSO_4(aq) + H_2O(l)$

9 Electrolysis

1

Solution	Positive electrode	Negative electrode	Evidence for this...
copper(II) chloride	chlorine	copper	(positive electrode) bubbling at electrode which bleaches damp litmus paper
			(negative electrode) brown/pink substance on electrode
copper(II) sulfate	oxygen	copper	(positive electrode) bubbling at electrode which doesn't bleach litmus paper
			(negative electrode) brown/pink substance on electrode
sodium chloride	chlorine	hydrogen	(positive electrode) bubbling at electrode which bleaches damp litmus paper
			(negative electrode) bubbling at electrode which doesn't bleach damp litmus paper
sodium sulfate	oxygen	hydrogen	(positive electrode) bubbling at electrode which doesn't bleach damp litmus paper
			(negative electrode) bubbling at electrode which doesn't bleach damp litmus paper

2 Your own comparisons.

3 Hydrogen gas: use a lit wooden splint/spill – it should go out with a pop.

Oxygen gas: use a glowing wooden splint/spill – it should relig

10 Temperature changes

1–3 Your own results.

4 The volume of hydrochloric acid will be 30 cm³ (as this is the initial volume and doesn't change). The volume of sodium hydroxide will depend on your graph – it should be the volu at the point where the lines of best fit cross.

5 At this point, no reaction is taking place. The acid has been used up and sodium hydroxide is now in excess. It is this excess, colder, sodium hydroxide which lowers the temperature.

Use a digital temperature sensor so the reading can more easily be seen going up and down. (This will also increase the precision of the temperature readings.)

Look at your graph and find the region where the lines of best fit cross. Read off the volume of sodium hydroxide at this point. Repeat the investigation but add 1 cm³ of sodium hydroxide at a time (rather than 5 cm³), using volumes approximately 5 cm³ either side of the maximum value read from your graph.

1 Rates of reaction

Part 1

Your own results.

Your own graphs. Both curves of best fit should rise steadily and then level off at about the same point. The curve for the higher concentration of acid should rise more steeply and level off sooner.

The reaction has finished at the point where the line on the graph levels off and becomes horizontal.

Increasing the concentration increases the rate of the reaction (makes the reaction faster).

The higher acid concentration (2.0 mol/dm³) produced a larger amount of gas in a shorter time, so the line drawn on the graph relating to these results was steeper at the start.

One possible source of error is measuring the volume of gas (which is difficult because of the bubbles in the measuring cylinder. Other answers are possible.)

Measure the volume of gas produced for a longer time, or measure larger volumes of gas. Other answers are possible.

Part 2

Your own results.

Your own graph. The graph should show a curve, starting high on the left (at a low concentration of sodium thiosulfate) and decreasing to the bottom right (at a high concentration of sodium thiosulfate).

a The rate increases quickly as the concentration of sodium thiosulfate increases.

b The graph shows that the time for the reaction decreases as the concentration increases; this means the rate of reaction increases.

The time taken would halve.

Your own view, depending on other results.

Your own answer. Both experiments should show that increasing the concentration increases the rate of reaction.

Measurement of time and measurement of volume of solutions.

Errors with recording time could be reduced by repeating the experiment more times. Errors with measuring the volume of solution could be reduced by using burettes and/or pipettes. Other answers are possible.

2 Chromatography

–4 Your own results.

Your answer will depend on the inks used. Look for any black inks which did not separate into a number of colours – if the ink remained as one main dot, it was a pure colour.

Your answer will depend on the inks used. Similar coloured dyes in the same location on your chromatography paper are likely to contain the same chemical compound.

The graphite from the pencil will not dissolve in the solvent (water), so it will not interfere with the results. The pencil line is also helpful when working out the R_f values, as it gives a clear point from which to take measurements.

So you knew which pen/original colour of ink was used to produce each spot of ink.

So the water will rise up the paper and dissolves the dyes.

13 Water purification

1 Likely answers are:

	Sample	Flame test (positive metal ions)	Nitric acid/silver nitrate test (negative halide ions)
Before	Salty water	yellow indicating sodium (ions) present	white indicating chloride (ions) present
After	Distilled water	no colour change visible (various metal ions not present)	remains clear (so no halide ions present)

2 Your own answer and explanation.

3 Use universal indicator (UI) or a pH meter to test the pH of the sample after distillation. The sample should be neutral (pH of 7).

OR

Heat the sample and record the temperature at which it boils. Pure water boils at 100 °C.

4 Your answer should include:

liquid is heated until it boils; liquid/water evaporates and turns into steam (water vapour); steam is pure water vapour; the steam/vapour passes into the condenser, where it cools down; as the vapour cools, it turns back into a liquid; the pure water collects as the distillate; anything dissolved in the water should remain in the conical flask.

14 Specific heat capacity

1–5 Your own results.

6 There are various explanations for the experimental results not being the same as published values. Discounting any errors made during the calculation stage (e.g. working out the correct gradient or plotting points correctly), there are other parts of the investigation that increase the chance of deviation. These include: difficulty reading the thermometer at the start (often it is below the level of the block and needs to be raised so it can be read); difficulty reading fluctuating ammeter and voltmeter readings, this will result in an inaccurate power value for the heater. The biggest source of error in this investigation is likely to be loss of thermal energy to surroundings. Unless the block has insulation across the top as well as a round the sides it will lose thermal energy and the results will be inaccurate.

15 Resistance

Part 1

1–3 Your own results.

4 As the length of the wire increases, so does the resistance;

or resistance is proportional to length (if their graph goes through origin);

or as length doubles so does resistance (if appropriate to their graph).

5 Your own explanation.

6 **a** Your own answer.

b The closer the points are to the line of best fit, the better the quality of the data you have gathered.

7 Your own conclusion.

8 Systematic: zero error on ammeter or voltmeter.
Random: the length of a wire is measured incorrectly.

Part 2

1 The total resistance of the circuit has increased.

2 The total resistance of the circuit is less than the resistance of the individual resistors.

3   Adding more resistors in series *increases* the total resistance in the circuit because the current through the resistors is *reduced* but the total potential difference across them remains the *same*. Adding more resistors in parallel *decreases* the total resistance because the total current through the resistors is increased *but* the total potential difference across them is *unchanged*.

4   **a**   Total resistance would increase.

    b   Total resistance would decrease.

16 Current–voltage characteristics

Tasks 1–3

1–2   For each task: your own results.

3   **a**   As potential difference changes, the current changes by the same percentage, i.e. current is proportional to potential difference. The graph is a straight line (gradient is constant) going through the origin because the resistance stays the same / is constant.

    b   A potential difference across a filament lamp causes a current to flow through it. The current causes the filament to heat up and glow. The greater the potential difference, the more current flows and the hotter the filament becomes. As the filament heats up, its resistance increases. This means that when the potential difference changes, the current does not change by the same percentage (the two variables are not in direction proportion). The graph starts to plateau at either end (gradient gets less).

    c   A diode has a low resistance if the potential difference is in one direction but a very high resistance if the potential difference is in the opposite direction. This means current can only flow in one direction. The resistance is usually high at negative and very small potential differences, but a diode behaves like a resistor above a certain positive potential differences; the current increases rapidly with voltage after 0.7 V.

4   Possible answers include: check for zero error on ammeter and voltmeter; prevent components heating up by switching off the power when not recording values.

5   Possible answers include: take multiple readings and work out a mean; use a datalogger to take readings at multiple potential differences and generate a graph.

6   Your own comparisons and explanation.

17 Density

Task 1

1–4   Your own results.

Task 2

1–2   Your own results.

Task 3

1–2   Your own results.

3   Your own results. The range of densities for the solids tested is likely to have been greater than the range of densities for the liquids.

4   The answer depends on the materials tested. You could point out that, in general, solids are more dense than liquids, although there are some solids that are less dense. Very good answers may also suggest whether each solid will float or sink in the different liquids tested.

18 Force and extension

1–4   Your own results. Your answer should talk about the range of data and how close points are to the line of best fit.

5   The spring with the larger spring constant should feel stiffer.

6   Suspend object from one of the springs. Record the extension of the spring. Use the graph from **2** to read the force required to bring about this extension. Use $W = mg$ calculate the mass of the object. (Could just divide the v for force in N by 10 to get the mass in kg.)

7   Your own results.

19 Acceleration

Part 1

1   Student's own results.

2   Student's own conclusion.

3   Yes if 3 matches the student's hypothesis.

Part 2

1   Student's own results.

2   Student's own conclusion.

3   Yes if 3 matches the student's hypothesis.

4   Newton's second law states $F = ma$ (student's own conclusion from results)

5   Timing errors (reaction time dependent) random.

Friction of bench/wheels/pulley systematic.

Measurement of mass (random unless each mass is reweighed).

6   Repeat the experiments and take an average, repeat any anomalous results.

Use light gates and a datalogger.

20 Waves

Part 1

1–2   Your own results.

3   Your results may vary because of different water depths (and different values of frequency/wavelength for the se of waves).

4   There may be less than one wave in a second/any errors counting the waves are spread out over 10 s, so this will g a more accurate value.

5   It is difficult to measure the wavelength while the waves are moving. The camera 'freezes' the motion of the waves so it is easier to make a precise and accurate measurement.

6   Answers are likely to relate to the speed of the wave; it is difficult to measure an accurate time when something is moving fast. Suggestions could include using a video camera with a time displayed.

Part 2

1–2   Your own results.

3   You could justify either answer: the wavelength, as this is obtained from a static measurement of the rod; the frequency, as this is measured electronically.

4   Your own table.

5   The sound travels too fast to use a stop clock/human reaction time would introduce errors greater than the tin being measured.

21 Radiation and absorption

1   Your own results.

2   Your graph should show curved lines with the gradient reduci as the temperature drops.

3   The rate of cooling decreases as the temperature drops.

4   You should have concluded that tubes covered with dark, dull paper are better at emitting radiation than tubes covered in light or shiny paper. Your answers should relate the emission radiation to the cooling rates shown on your graph.

5   Your answers should discuss any anomalous (strange or unexpected) readings and how much difference in cooling rat there is between the different tubes.

6   No, only four different papers have been tested.